郭月英 炖补 100锅

100道对症食疗炖补汤锅，
烹调简单快速、美味又营养。
每天利用30分钟好汤上桌，
轻松改造体质、增强抗病力，
照顾全家，好健康、好简单。

郭月英◎著

陈丽玲◎文字撰写·李家雄◎监制

辽宁科学技术出版社

本书由中国台湾三味文化事业有限公司授权辽宁科学技术出版社出版、发行简体中文版，著作权合同登记号为06–2004年第179号

图书在版编目（CIP）数据

炖补100锅/郭月英著.—沈阳：辽宁科学技术出版社，2005.1

ISBN 7–5381–4287–8

Ⅰ．炖…　Ⅱ．郭…　Ⅲ．保健–汤菜–菜谱
Ⅳ．TS972.161

中国版本图书馆CIP数据核字（2004）第133147号

出版发行：辽宁科学技术出版社
　　　　　　（地址：沈阳市和平区十一纬路25号　邮编：110003）
印　刷　者：沈阳市第二印刷厂
经　销　者：各地新华书店
幅面尺寸：185mm×235mm
印　　张：6
字　　数：138千字
印　　数：1～6 000
出版时间：2005年1月第1版
印刷时间：2005年4月第2次印刷
责任编辑：李丽梅　姚福龙　邱利伟
封面设计：杜　江
版式设计：袁　姝
责任校对：姚喜荣

定　　价：25.00元

联系电话：024-23284360
邮购热线：024-23284502　23284357
E-mail：lkzzb@mail.lnpgc.com.cn
http://www.lnkj.com.cn

适症选对食补
轻松改造体质

随着季节气候的变化，自然而然会想到吃炖补来建立雄厚的体质以养精蓄锐、预防疾病。十全大补鸡、药炖排骨、当归鸭、麻油鸡等琳琅满目的炖补药膳，让人无法抉择到底该吃什么？如果不补呢，又好像欠缺某些养分，吃多了又怕补过头，类似这种矛盾的心态常常发生。

其实正确地"进补"，应该是着重辨明个人体质状况，选择合适的健康膳食来协调五脏六腑正常运作的机制。

物质丰富的现代生活，反而容易有失眠、躁郁、文明病、慢性病、癌变等症状与疾病发生在周围亲朋好友的身上，甚至自己也可能深受其苦，在这种环境之下，更要懂得自我健康管理的重要性。所谓病从口入，但更坚信病亦能从口愈，除了药物之外，饮食调整与疗养，相信绝对能防止人体免疫力减弱，对症进补调养得宜，自然能提升自体免疫力，免除病痛。

在众多的食疗方中，我归纳整理出十大方向，从最基本的改善体质、消除疲劳的膳食着手，进而为现代人开启另一扇有效舒解压力、放松心灵的饮食窗；一旦压力能释放、心情愉悦，则抗老防衰、养生益寿、疏筋活血、提升睡眠品质，无疑像一连串的增值效益，环环相扣，相得益彰。

这本食谱同时还传递另一项保健观念，所谓胃肠为身体后天之基本，要提升体能、增强抵抗力，健胃整肠是不容忽视的一环，否则无法吸收利用有效的营养成分，以架构组织器官、巩固身体的防护网；再者，免疫力降低容易受流感之患而时常感冒，本书亦有相关章节对其进行探讨，甚至银发族的骨质疏松症以及癌变等都一一列出，提供适症进补的食疗方来补强，无论是选单一章节或全面性择取，都能满足不同症候或个人体况的需求。

每道食谱皆以深入浅出、解析详尽的特色，从功效阐述、材料介绍到做法步骤，以至于适合对象或相关禁忌等，再加上取材容易、简单易做，相信只要用心，同时配合规律的作息、适度的运动，并随时保持愉快的心情，必能减少疾病的威胁，享受健康的生活。

郭月英

目录contents

PART3 舒解压力，放松心情

PART4 延缓老化，养颜美白

PART5 强身益寿，养生保健

PART6 舒眠解压，疏筋活血

PART7 健胃整肠，帮助消化

PART8 预防伤风感冒

炖补
100锅

目录 contents

补得巧，补得刚刚好！

注重生活保健最好的方式是通过天然食材搭配食物性中药材来进行缓和的调整体质，可谓"食借药力、药助食威"，两者相辅相成，可充分发挥滋补保健作用，达到强化造血机制、促进气血循环、增强免疫系统功能、降低感染疾病的功效。

选对食物能提高免疫力

每个人的体质及症状会随着生活习惯的改变而改变，适时适量补充身体所需的养分，可避免病毒潜伏。拒绝影响健康的食物，如过量的酒精、咖啡、油炸物、烟、含高量动物性油脂及精致高热量的糕饼、甜点、零食、高糖碳酸饮料等，这些食物不仅无法提供身体所需的营养素，反而容易让体内组织器官堆积更多的油脂及不良菌群，减低其他营养素的功效，所以食材的选择是不可忽视的。

平时除了要拒绝抗营养素的食物，选择能提高免疫力、增强活力的食物，如蕈类：草菇、猴头菇、木耳；十字花科蔬菜：如绿花椰菜、甘蓝、芥蓝菜等；含有辣素类：像葱、姜、大蒜、洋葱、芥末等；海洋植物类：像海带、海藻、海菜及含嗜乳酸杆菌的酸奶等；坚果类、全谷类、黄豆制品、深黄深绿蔬果、番茄、柑橘类、萝卜、苦瓜、地瓜、芦笋、牛蒡等都值得推荐，而黄芪、山药、枸杞、大枣、人参、当归等，经临床证实均能提升免疫力，是维持良好体力的药材。

每天花少许时间为自己及家人炖补，并选择合适食材适时补充养分，既可满足口欲，也能让全家人洋溢着幸福、满足、快乐，这是再多的金钱也比不上的。

让你补得巧，补得刚刚好

"进补"是利用传统中药或食材来改善体质、纠正阴阳气血偏差、协调脏腑的运作功能、疏通经络的循环作用，达到预防疾病、延年益寿的功效。进补要补得巧，补得恰到好处，虽然一年四季随时都是进补期，但关键在于如何配合时令，认识身体状况的转换，而掌握取得最佳效果的契机。

春天要平和进补、夏天适合清凉之补，秋天则宜温顺进补，冬天可是要积极且机动性调补；尤其"立冬"、"冬至"两大节气，更是让我们的身心达到最佳状态的良好机会，此时要选择质性平和、滋补效果佳的食材和药材相配合，为身体填充能量，做好应付寒冬，抵抗病菌的准备；再搭配适量的运动，就能健健康康、快快乐乐过生活，而特殊体质也可依状况进行调理。

如果自觉身体有多种状况，或某一状况特别显著者，例如：经常手足冰冷、背寒畏冷、脸色苍白、食欲不振、容易感冒、动辄疲倦、注意力不集中、习惯性腹泻、经期症候群、更年期症候群或是男女性功能失调、早衰老化明显者，都需要有适当的补养调理，则可依本书所提供的各类炖补汤品佳肴，选择适合自己身心状况的进行炖补，持续一季地保养，只待春暖花开，相信会展现另一番新的身心景象。

PART1

改善体质，增强抵抗力

　　身体健康需视个人免疫力的强弱而定，免疫力则取决于先天性遗传基因；但后天饮食调整对改造体质、增加抗病力是有很大帮助的。

　　平时多摄取含蛋白质、维生素A、维生素C、维生素E及矿物质的食物，如山药、苹果、海带、甜椒等，可增加免疫细胞中的淋巴细胞数目，刺激身体制造干扰素，增强抗体，减弱自由基活动力，使免疫系统"坚强牢固"。

　　经常运动、排除压力，并远离降低免疫力的高脂、高糖、烟酒、咖啡等食物，也能提升免疫力，增强抵抗力。

01 黄芪枸杞鸡汤

——提高免疫力，抗癌抑菌

材料：鸡腿1只
药材：黄芪20克，枸杞10克，大枣8枚
调味料：盐1小匙

●适合对象：一般人都适合，特别是容易疲劳、工作繁重、课业压力大及过劳族群更需加强补给。

做法：

1. 鸡腿剁块，放入滚水中汆烫，捞起洗净沥干。

2. 鸡腿、全部药材放入锅中，加1500毫升水以大火煮沸，转小火继续炖30分钟。

3. 起锅前加盐调味即成。

黄芪能促进生理代谢，活络细胞吞噬细菌的能力；枸杞能促进造血功能，增加白细胞数量，搭配富含蛋白质、矿物质和维生素的鸡肉炖汤能改善全身营养状态，增强体能，提高免疫力、抗老防衰、抗癌抑菌，同时保护肝脏，维持人体良好的代谢和排毒功能。

材料：鲍鱼1只，鸡腿1只，山药300克

药材：大枣8枚

调味料：盐1小匙

做法：

1. 鸡腿剁块，放入滚水中汆烫，捞起洗净沥干。山药削皮、洗净、切块。鲍鱼切片。

2. 鸡腿、大枣放入锅中，加1200毫升水以大火煮沸，转小火继续煮15分钟。

3. 加入山药继续煮10分钟，放入鲍鱼片，加盐调味即成。

鲍鱼能维护肝、肾正常运作功能，有效迅速分解废物及排泄有毒物质，净空体内毒素，让免疫系统维持最佳化，搭配山药，有预防过敏、消炎、调节机能、增强体魄、改善体质的作用，亦能缓和慢性气管炎，调节性功能失调。

02 鲍鱼山药鸡汤

——排出体内毒素，改善体质

03 苹果干贝鸡汤

——调理五脏，改善吸收

材料：
苹果1个，干贝5粒，鸡腿1只
调味料：
盐1小匙

●适合对象：老少咸宜，特别是容易心烦口渴、失眠多梦、消化不良及有水肿现象的人可经常食用。

做法：

1. 鸡腿剁块，放入滚水中汆烫，捞起洗净沥干。
2. 干贝洗净加200毫升水放入电饭锅蒸软。苹果削皮洗净，切块。
3. 鸡腿、干贝、苹果加1200毫升水以大火煮沸，再转小火继续炖25分钟，起锅前加盐调味即成。

干贝含丰富的磷，能促进细胞生长及修复，协助脂肪、碳水化合物代谢；苹果是最好的保健水果，能调节便秘、腹泻、抗氧化及改善胃肠炎。苹果干贝鸡汤能调理五脏亏虚，改善营养吸收状态，提供人体能量与活力，是维护优良体质不可缺少的好汤品。

材料：乌鸡腿1只

药材：熟地黄4克，当归4克，白芍4克，川芎4克，党参4克，茯苓4克，白术4克，甘草4克，黄芪4克，桂枝4克，大枣6枚

调味料：米酒50毫升

● 适合对象：病后、产后、手术后虚弱者，接受化学治疗或放射性治疗者，贫血、闭经、衰老快速者皆适用。

做法：

1. 鸡腿剁块，放入滚水中氽烫，捞起洗净沥干。

2. 鸡腿、全部药材放入锅中，加1500毫升水以大火煮沸，再转小火继续炖40分钟。

3. 加入米酒调味即成。

此汤品是补中气、养肝气、调理气血两虚之代表汤，能增进造血功能、促进新陈代谢、强壮体能、预防人体机能衰退，增强免疫力与抗病力，有抗癌、抗辐射的作用，并可活络中枢神经，减轻忧劳思虑、烦闷抑郁，缓和化疗副作用，无论食补或调理都适合。

04 十全大补乌鸡汤

——调理气血，预防机能衰退

05 冬瓜干贝鸭汤

——利尿消肿，调节体弱耗损

材料：
冬瓜300克，鸭肉300克，干贝5粒
调味料：
盐1小匙

●适合对象：虚胖、尿少、容易口渴、运动不足者可多食用，唯体质极为虚寒者少食用。

做法：

1. 鸭肉剁块，放入滚水中汆烫，捞起洗净沥干。
2. 干贝洗净加200毫升水放入电饭锅蒸软。冬瓜削皮去籽，洗净切块。
3. 鸭肉、冬瓜、干贝加1200毫升水以大火煮沸，转小火继续炖30分钟，起锅前加盐调味即成。

冬瓜含较多量的维生素C，能清热解毒、利尿消肿、降火气、抗氧化；干贝益肾和胃，调理体弱耗损、神经失调、提升睡眠品质；鸭肉是提振男性阳气的重要食材，能使小便顺畅，改善身体浮肿、口渴、心慌、失眠、头晕眼花症状。冬瓜干贝鸭汤能预防体内致癌物质的形成，对调节体弱耗损、滋补脏腑、助安眠有一定的功效。

材料：
排骨600克
药材：
党参10克，黄芪10克，熟地黄10克，当归8克，川芎4克、
肉桂4克

●适合对象：发育期少男少女、中年人及银发族都适宜。

做法：
1. 排骨放入滚水中氽烫，捞起洗净沥干。
2. 排骨、全部药材放入锅中，加1500毫升水以大火煮沸，
转小火继续炖40分钟即成。

排骨富含蛋白质、磷、铁、钙，能强筋健骨，促进生长发育；党参可补中益气；黄芪补气强心，增强免疫功能；熟地黄可滋阴养血、调经理带；当归调血活血、止痛去淤；川芎能改善血液循环、稳定心绪；肉桂调和体质、温经止痹。药炖排骨能调节内分泌，刺激生长激素的分泌，并改善骨质预防疏松症状，是老少咸宜的最佳补养汤品。

06 药炖排骨
——强筋健胃，预防骨质疏松

07 海带排骨汤

——抵抗感染，帮助免疫功能维持正常

材料：
海带结200克，胡萝卜1根，排骨600克
调味料：
盐1小匙

●适合对象：人人皆宜，皮肤枯燥，指甲无光泽，蛀牙或成长发育阶段可加强补给。

做法：

1. 排骨放入滚水中汆烫，捞起洗净沥干。

2. 胡萝卜削皮洗净，切块。海带结洗净。

3. 排骨、胡萝卜、海带结放入锅中，加1200毫升水以大火煮沸，转小火继续炖30分钟。

4. 起锅前加盐调味即成。

海带含碘、微量的氟，能促进细胞氧化作用，燃烧多余脂肪，使神经、肌肉正常运作，维持生长及生育能力处于正常状态，还能促进牙齿、指甲、毛发、皮肤的健康，搭配富含胡萝卜和含大量蛋白质、维生素B族的排骨，能有抵抗感染的作用，有助于免疫系统功能维持正常。

材料：

菜豆110克、红甜椒1个、玉米笋5支、马铃薯1个、香菇3朵、排骨225克

调味料：

盐1/2小匙

做法：

1. 排骨放入滚水中汆烫，捞起洗净沥干。

2. 菜豆洗净。玉米笋洗净，斜切成两段。马铃薯洗净削皮，切块。

3. 香菇洗净去蒂，切半。红甜椒洗净切半，去籽，切块。

4. 菜豆、玉米笋、马铃薯、香菇、排骨放入锅，加1200毫升水以大
　　火煮沸，转小火继续炖20分钟。

5. 放入红甜椒继续煮5分钟，加盐调味即成。

五色健康食物的颜色可分为绿、红、黄、白、黑等，分别助益肝、心、脾、肺、肾等五
脏，均衡摄取有助于五脏气血循环功能运作正常及促进新陈代谢，并有利于人体对营养
素的吸收与利用，增强体力、改善体质、提升免疫功能。

08

五色彩蔬汤
——帮助五脏气血循环运作正常

●适合对象：老少咸宜，
且性味平和、营养丰富，
可作为平时调补的汤品，素
食者只要不加排骨，一样
可以获得营养美味的效
果。

09

海带山药绿豆汤

——止渴解毒，避免代谢率降低

材料：

干品海带150克，山药225克，绿豆225克

调味料：

冰糖100克

●适合对象：一般人皆合适，尤其是甲状腺分泌不足或肿大者应常食用；虚胖、动作迟缓、反应迟钝者也可多食用，唯胀气、虚寒者少食。

做法：

1. 山药削皮洗净，切小块。海带泡发洗净。

2. 绿豆洗净，加1200毫升水，放入海带以大火煮沸，转小火继续煮20分钟。

3. 加入山药以中火煮沸，转小火继续煮15分钟，放入冰糖煮溶即成。

海带富含碘，可预防心智反应迟钝、活力不足及发胖；山药能强肾固精，改善衰弱、性功能失调；绿豆能利尿消肿、清热解毒，有利体内废物毒素排出，预防致癌物质形成。海带山药绿豆汤能维持甲状腺激素分泌机能正常，避免基本代谢率降低，调节身体机能，赋予机体活力，令人显得有朝气。

材料：

新鲜百合2颗，莲子300克，大枣10枚

调味料：

冰糖100克

做法：

1.莲子洗净，加1200毫升水，放入大枣，以大火煮沸，转小火继续煮30分钟。

2.百合剥瓣，修去老边，洗净，放入锅中续煮5分钟。

3.加入冰糖煮溶即成。

新鲜百合能镇静止咳、调理体质虚弱，也能缓和妇女更年期症候群，如情绪起伏、失眠多梦；莲子能滋补养神、养心益肾及调节妇女病；大枣能活血调经、补气宁神、提振体力、改善气血不足。百合莲枣甜汤能防范忧郁焦躁、调节更年期症状、防治呼吸道感染、慢性支气管炎及增强活力和体能。

10 百合莲枣甜汤

——养心宁神，镇静止咳

PART2

消除疲劳，恢复体力

　　现代人工作繁重、压力大，常饱受劳苦之患，除了要有适宜的宣泄途径之外，还要睡眠充足、适当运动、心情愉悦、经常保持笑容，并摄取均衡的饮食来增强人体免疫力，才可减轻疲劳和压力。

　　维生素B_1被称为精神性维生素，维生素B_2能缓解紧张压力，维生素B_{12}能除烦解忧，维生素E能减轻疲劳，还有多种矿物质都有此食疗效果，因此，我们平时可多吃绿色蔬菜、柑橘类、番茄、牛乳、蛋类、猪肉、牛肉、全麦、燕麦等，而这些都是消除疲劳、缓解压力、增强身心适应力的好食材。

材料：鸡腿1只

药材：人参片10克，大枣8枚

调味料：盐1小匙

●适合对象：体虚乏力、营养失调、劳累过度、贫血、失眠多梦、食欲不振、妇女失血过多、头晕腰酸、面黄消瘦、手脚冰冷者都适宜，唯体质燥热、重感冒或严重腹泻者不宜。

做法：

1. 鸡腿剁块，放入滚水中汆烫，捞起洗净沥干。

2. 鸡腿、人参片、大枣放入锅中，加1500毫升水以大火煮沸，转小火继续炖30分钟。

3. 起锅前加盐调味即成。

人参大补元气，能排除体内毒素，刺激内分泌腺，吸收维生素和矿物质，对失眠、疲劳、血液循环不良、血压不正常等皆有功效。经常食用参片大枣鸡汤能增进食欲、宁心安神、助安眠、增强活力、快速恢复体力。

11 参片大枣鸡汤

——增进身心活力，快速恢复体力

12 党参竹笙鸡汤

——提神健脑，减轻疲劳

材料：鸡腿1只，竹笙40克
药材：党参20克，枸杞10克
调味料：盐1小匙

做法：

1. 鸡腿剁块，放入滚水中余烫，捞起洗净沥干。

2. 竹笙泡发，去伞帽，洗净拧干切段。

3. 鸡腿、党参加1200毫升水以大火煮沸，再转小火
继续炖20分钟。

4. 放入竹笙、枸杞续炖5分钟，起锅前加盐调味即成。

●适合对象：人人都适宜，经常精神疲惫、活动力差、脸色苍白、须发早白、心悸、健忘者可以多食用。

党参能增强身体的活力，对神经系统有兴奋作用，能提神健脑、减轻疲劳，提高抗病能力，增强体内杀菌的功效。搭配有多种生理活性的枸杞、可激发淋巴细胞转换的竹笙，更能提高人体的防御能力。

材料：

冬瓜300克，蛤蜊300克，鸡腿1只，姜1段

调味料：

盐1/2小匙

●适合对象：热燥体质、容易上火、小便不顺、便秘、水肿者可常食；胃寒、虚弱、习惯性腹泻者不宜。

做法：

1. 蛤蜊浸泡淡盐水，吐沙洗净，捞起沥干。冬瓜削皮去籽，洗净切块。姜洗净，切片。

2. 鸡腿剁块，放入滚水中，氽烫，捞起洗净沥干。

3. 鸡腿、冬瓜、姜片放入锅中，加1500毫升水以大火煮沸，转小火继续炖25分钟。

4. 加入蛤蜊转中火煮至开口，加盐调味即成。

蛤蜊和鸡肉含有丰富的蛋白质和钙、铁等矿物质。蛋白质是构成白细胞和抗体的主要成分，一旦缺乏会使免疫细胞中的淋巴细胞数减少，使免疫机能下降；铁质也是淋巴组织正常运作的要素。此汤品有活血补虚、消水肿、强筋骨、减轻疲劳、改善小便不畅及强化免疫机能的功效。

13 蛤蜊冬瓜鸡汤

——活血补虚，缓解疲劳

14 四君子土鸡汤
——补阳益气，健胃助食

材料：

土鸡腿1只，生姜1段

药材：

党参10克，白术10克，茯苓10克，甘草8克

做法：

1. 鸡腿剁块，放入滚水中汆烫，捞起洗净沥干。生姜洗净切片。

2. 生姜、鸡腿和全部药材放入锅中，加1500毫升水以大火煮沸，转小火继续炖30分钟。

3. 起锅前加盐调味即成。

●适合对象：胃肠机能虚弱、消化不良、胃溃疡、胃下垂者，儿童营养不良、发育迟缓及偏食者都适合。

四君子土鸡汤是健胃补脾的强壮剂，改善阳气不足、食欲不振、营养不良、四肢乏力、容易疲劳、面色苍白、说话有气无力等现象；可促进人体对营养成分的吸收与利用，增进胃肠消化、缓和胃溃疡、胃下垂，能兴奋中枢神经，减轻疲劳。

材料：羊肉600克，老姜1段
药材：当归10克，黄芪20克
调味料：盐1小匙

●适合对象：一般血虚或病后气血不足、肢体疼痛及产后腹冷、发痛、发烧者都适合，也可以当做冬令进补的汤品，唯体型壮硕、火气大者不宜。

做法：

1. 羊肉放入滚水中氽烫，捞起洗净沥干。老姜洗净，切片。

2. 羊肉、姜片、当归、黄芪放入锅中，加1500毫升水以大火煮沸，转小火继续炖40分钟。

3. 起锅前加盐调味即成。

当归、黄芪是补血圣品，能调节子宫机能，调经、安胎、助孕效果佳，并有提高抗病力的作用。羊肉则是补阳佳品。此汤品不但是坐月子时的重要补品，也是妇女调经理带、银发族改善气血循环的良汤，还能改善产后虚弱、腹部冷痛、腰酸背痛、末梢循环不良、四肢冰冷等症状，并可预防老人机能衰退。

15 归芪生姜羊肉汤

——促进血液循环，改善四肢冰冷

材料：牛腩600克，洋葱1个，胡萝卜1
　　　根，番茄1个
调味料：酱油3大匙，红糖1大匙、辣豆
　　　瓣酱1大匙，豆瓣酱2大匙

做法：

1. 牛腩洗净切块，洋葱剥掉红膜去根须，
　　洗净切块。

2. 胡萝卜削皮洗净，切块。番茄洗净，
　　切块。

3. 牛腩、洋葱、胡萝卜、番茄、调味料
　　放入锅中，加1600毫升水以大火煮沸，
　　转小火继续炖40分钟即成。

16

红烧牛肉汤

—— 快速恢复体力，预防贫血

●适合对象：男女老
少咸宜。健康状态不
良、贫血、焦虑烦躁
者可多食用。

材料：韩式泡菜150克，鲜虾10尾，蛤
　　　蜊10个，蟹脚肉75克，鱿鱼1/2尾

做法：

1. 鲜虾剪去须脚洗净。蛤蜊浸泡淡盐水，
　　吐沙洗净，捞起沥干。

2. 鱿鱼洗净，切十字斜纹，再切片。蟹
　　脚肉洗净。

3. 韩式泡菜放入锅中，加1200毫升水煮
　　沸，放入鲜虾、蛤蜊、蟹脚肉、鱿鱼
　　煮熟即成。

泡菜海鲜锅

—— 顺畅肝气，提振精神

●适合对象：食欲不振、
营养失调者，可借此汤品
诱发食欲；唯胃酸分泌失
调、胃肠溃疡者不宜。

17

材料：哈什蚂（雪蛤）1只，莲子150克，
　　　大枣10枚

调味料：冰糖100克

做法：

1. 哈什蚂自腹部剪开，剥取哈什蚂油，以
　清水泡发，挑去杂质沥干。

2. 莲子、大枣洗净放入锅中，加1500毫升
　水以大火煮沸，转小火继续炖25分钟。

3. 放入哈什蚂继续炖5分钟，加入冰糖拌
　匀即成。

●适合对象：人人皆宜，
精力衰退、体力不济、瘦
干枯黑者尤其适合；亦适
合为产后辅助食品。

雪蛤莲子甜汤

——改善虚弱，充实体力

紫米莲子粥

——镇静安神，滋补气血

材料：紫米（或黑米）1杯（电饭锅量杯），
　　　莲子150克

调味料：红糖120克

做法：

1. 紫米、莲子洗净，放入锅中，加1500毫
　升水，以大火煮沸，再转小火继续炖30
　分钟（每隔3～5分钟搅拌数下以防沾
　锅）。

2. 加红糖煮溶即成。

●适合对象：一般人皆
宜，唯儿童、老年人、病
后疗养期、肠胃消化功能
失调者可浅尝，但不宜
多吃或常吃。

20

黄芪海参猪舌汤

——改善体质，增强抗病力

材料：猪舌1个，海参300克，胡萝卜1段，青江菜1棵

药材：黄芪20克

调味料：盐1小匙

做法：

1. 猪舌刮净舌苔，放入滚水中氽烫，捞起洗净，切块。

2. 海参自腹部划开，去肠洗净，放入滚水中氽烫，捞起切块。

3. 胡萝卜削皮洗净、切花片，青江菜去荖叶洗净，切段。

4. 黄芪加1500毫升水以大火煮沸，放入猪舌、胡萝卜转中小火继续炖20分钟。

5. 加入海参继续炖5分钟，放入青江菜煮沸，加盐调味即成。

●适合对象：一般皆宜；气血不调、过劳、虚弱、说话有气无力、发肤干涩、提早衰老者可多食用。

海参富含优质蛋白质，能滋阴补血、健阳润燥，维持生命的能量，降低感染机会；黄芪可改善营养失调，增加机体抵抗力。黄芪海参猪舌汤能促进身体吸收养分、改善体质、增强抗病力，是最适宜过劳成虚、久虚成疾者服用的滋补汤品。

PART3

舒解压力，放松心情

　　繁忙的社会造成现代人压力过大、精神紧张，忧郁症患者与日俱增，自杀人数居高不下，暴力倾向愈来愈突显，这些都是我们不可忽视的现象。

　　运动、休闲、阅读有助于排解压力、调节心情，而适当的饮食方法能使解压效果大增，性味清凉的蔬果能消暑散热、舒缓压力；维生素B族、维生素C、钙、磷、铁、镁及碘等矿物质有缓解失眠、增添活力、减轻疲劳、抵抗忧郁、降低压力指数等作用。你可依个人身体需求，摄取有利于身心健康的食物，让自己天天保持心情的愉悦，将压力转化为动力，并增强抗病力。

21 苦瓜菠萝炖鸡汤

——消除焦躁，提高免疫力

材料：苦瓜1根、菠萝225克，鸡腿1只

调味料：盐1小匙

做法：

1. 苦瓜切半去籽、洗净切块。菠萝削皮，切块。

2. 鸡腿剁块，放入滚水中氽烫，捞起洗净。

3. 苦瓜、菠萝、鸡腿放入锅中，加1500毫升水以大火煮沸，转小火继续炖30分钟，加盐调味即成。

●适合对象：一般人皆宜，尤其是火气大、青春痘脓肿、便秘、口臭、体味重者宜常食用；唯脾胃虚寒、慢性胃肠溃疡者则不宜。

苦瓜富含维生素C，是维护精神状态良好的优质食材；还含有蛋白酶，可刺激免疫细胞，加强抑制不正常细胞的能力；菠萝含有与胃液相似的酵素，有助于分解蛋白质，搭配鸡肉煮食，能消暑解毒、利水消肿、除烦解忧、消除焦躁，提高免疫力。

材料：新鲜鱼片300克，菠菜1棵
药材：甘草8克，小麦10克，大枣6枚
调味料：盐1小匙

做法：

1. 鱼片洗净沥干。菠菜去根须，洗净切段。

2. 全部药材放入锅中，加1200毫升水以大火煮沸，
转小火继续炖20分钟。

3. 加入鱼片转中火煮沸，放入菠菜煮2分钟，加
盐调味即成。

甘草、小麦、大枣是调理忧郁症及焦虑症的重要汤品，且养心安神效果佳，善于稳定情绪、
改善精神恍惚、烦躁不安、莫名悲伤欲哭、夜眠不安稳、疑神疑鬼、容易紧张、思虑过度
等现象，也适合调节妇女更年期症候群及遭逢重大变故后的身心调养。

22 甘麦大枣鱼汤

——缓解精神恍惚，烦躁不安

23 酸菜姜鸭汤

——疏肝解郁，消除疲劳

材料：

酸菜150克，鸭1/4只，姜1块

调味料：

盐适量

●适合对象：特别适合汗尿排泄失调、工作压力大、人际关系紧张及劳动量大者；唯胃肠虚弱、胃酸分泌失调或伤口恢复期不宜。

做法：

1. 鸭肉剁块，放入滚水中汆烫，捞起洗净。酸菜、姜洗净切片。
2. 鸭肉、酸菜、姜片放入锅中，加1500毫升水以大火煮沸，转小火继续炖30分钟。
3. 加盐调味即成。

酸菜是用芥菜腌渍而成，其酸味有疏肝解郁、减轻疲劳、刺激食欲的作用，搭配鸭肉，可利尿消肿、生津止渴，改善阳气不振、心慌、头晕、失眠、口渴不止等现象。此汤品能刺激肝气循环，快速代谢体内毒素，避免废物堆积，造成易疲劳、睡眠品质低落、情绪不稳定及肩颈酸痛等现象。

材料：猪脑1个
药材：天麻4克、枸杞10克
调味料：盐1/2小匙

做法：

1. 猪脑洗净，以牙签挑去薄膜和血丝。

2. 猪脑、天麻、枸杞放入碗盅，倒水盖满材料，加入
   调味料，以保鲜膜封住盅口。

3. 移入电饭锅，外锅加1杯水，待汤品炖熟后，继续
   焖15分钟即成。

猪脑含有比猪肉更丰富的磷、铁、钙质，能强化神经系统，维持心脏跳动频率，缓和失眠，消除疲劳，供给身体能量与活力，搭配天麻能防治晕眩、眼眶发黑、头痛、半身不遂、肢体麻木、癫痫抽搐，有明显镇静抗惊、改善耳鸣、关节疼痛的功效。

24 天麻猪脑汤
——改善头晕目眩、耳鸣、关节疼痛

材料：猪心1个

药材：参须10克，枸杞20克

调味料：盐1/2小匙

做法：

1. 猪心挤洗去血水，放入滚水中汆烫，捞起洗净，切片。

2. 参须、枸杞放入锅中，加1200毫升水以大火煮沸，转小火继续炖10分钟。

3. 加入猪心煮沸，加盐调味即成。

参须枸杞猪心汤

——缓解紧张，安神定惊

● 适合对象：一般人皆宜，经常面临较长期的工作挑战、课业压力、个性较内向、安静、情绪发泄途径较不通畅的人可多食用。

材料：猪肚1个

药材：桂圆75克，党参20克

做法：

1. 猪肚用盐搓洗干净，放入滚水中汆烫，捞起洗净，切大片。

2. 猪肚、党参放入锅中，加1500毫升水以大火煮沸，转小火继续炖40分钟。

3. 桂圆剥散放入锅中，继续炖10分钟即成（可酌加盐调味）。

● 适合对象：一般人皆宜；发育中男女、喜欢喝冷饮、胃口不佳、消化不良、精神萎靡、嗜睡懒动的人可多食用。

桂圆党参肚片汤

——改善虚弱，调和气血不足

材料：绿豆1杯（电饭锅量杯），豆腐1块，
　　　豆浆1000毫升

调味料：红糖100克

做法：

1. 绿豆洗净，加500毫升水以大火煮沸，
再转小火继续煮20分钟。

2. 加入豆浆转中火煮沸，豆腐切小块，放
入锅中继续煮5分钟（每2～3分钟搅拌数
下，以免沾锅）。

3. 放入红糖煮溶即成。

●适合对象：一
般人皆宜；有冠心病
史、胆固醇高、体质燥热、
皮肤过敏者适合常食用；
唯慢性肠胃炎、痛风、
糖尿病患者不宜。

27

豆浆豆腐绿豆汤
——减轻肝脏负担，活化细胞

椰肉枸杞甜汤
——除烦解忧，抗老防衰

材料：椰子1个、枸杞8克

调味料：冰糖80克

做法：

1. 椰子蒂头切开取汁，以汤匙刮下椰肉。

2. 椰汁、椰肉和枸杞放入锅中，加500毫
升水，以大火煮沸，转小火继续煮3分
钟。

3. 加冰糖煮溶即成。

●适合对象：一般
人皆宜，唯性稍偏凉，
脾胃虚弱、经常腹泻、呕吐、
晕虚眼黑的人不宜；青春痘
严重、汗臭、口臭明显，
牙龈浮肿的人可多食
用。

28

29

材料：排骨600克、干金针75克、黑木耳75克、青江菜1棵

调味料：盐1小匙

做法：

1. 排骨放入滚水中汆烫，捞起洗净沥干。干金针打结加清水浸泡10分钟，沥干水分。
2. 黑木耳洗净切片，青江菜洗净切段。
3. 排骨、金针、黑木耳放入锅中，加1500毫升水以大火煮沸，转小火继续炖30分钟。
4. 加入青江菜煮沸，加调味料即成。

金针木耳排骨汤
——改善忧郁焦虑，助安眠

●适合对象：一般人皆宜，特别是受重大打击或惊吓以及免疫力差、失眠、躁郁症的人可常食用。

材料：排骨375克，黄豆1/2杯（电饭锅量杯），糙米1/2杯

调味料：盐1小匙

做法：

1. 排骨放入滚水中汆烫，捞起洗净沥干。黄豆、糙米洗净沥干。
2. 排骨、黄豆、糙米放入锅中，加1500毫升水以大火煮沸，转小火继续炖30分钟。
3. 加入调味料即成。

黄豆糙米排骨汤
——缓和神经过敏，预防老人痴呆

30

●适合对象：一般人都合适，常抽烟、喝酒、记忆力衰退者可常吃，孕妇、哺乳期妇女及发育成长期男女更适合多吃。

PART4

延缓衰老，养颜美白

"哇！你看起来好年轻哦！"听起来多么令人兴奋的一句话。

其实想要延缓衰老并不难，只要平时多摄取含有强效抗氧化的维生素A、维生素C、维生素E，如番茄、芹菜、苹果、山药、小黄瓜等食物，并持续运动，保持愉悦的心情，则可去除体内有害的活性氧，防止细胞受到氧化而产生过氧化脂质，让催人衰老、破坏容颜、衍生慢性病、令细胞癌变的祸首有效地被箝制住；进而维持身心充足的抗氧化环境，自然可延缓衰老、养颜美容、活泼心智。

番茄豆芽猪尾汤

——预防角质老化，早生皱纹

材料：

番茄2个，黄豆芽300克，猪尾375克

调味料：

盐1小匙

做法：

1.番茄洗净去蒂，切块。黄豆芽去根须洗净，沥干。

2.猪尾剁块，放入滚水中汆烫，捞起洗净。

3.猪尾、黄豆芽、番茄放入锅中，加2000毫升水以大火煮沸，转小火继续炖25分钟。

4.加盐调味即成。

●适合对象：男女老少皆宜，经常曝晒、抽烟、高血压、糖尿病患者或在污浊环境中工作的人可常食用。

番茄含丰富的茄红素，是极重要的抗氧化物质，能减少自由基生成，延缓肌肤老化，同时能抗癌、保护心血管健康、预防多种慢性病；黄豆芽富含食物纤维，可促进胃肠蠕动，帮助体内快速排出残留的废物与毒素；猪尾的胶原蛋白，可使细胞更紧密结合，有效防御病毒侵袭、润泽肌肤，有预防角质老化、早生皱纹的作用。

材料：

青木瓜600克，排骨600克，大枣10枚

调味料：

盐1小匙

●适合对象：一般人皆宜，特别是发育期的少女及产后哺乳的妈妈更需要多食用。

做法：

1. 排骨放入滚水中汆烫，捞起洗净沥干。青木瓜削皮去籽，洗净切块。

2. 排骨、大枣加1500毫升水，以大火煮沸，转小火继续炖20分钟。

3. 加入木瓜继续炖10分钟，加盐调味即成。

青木瓜含有木瓜酵素，能分解蛋白质，让人体充分吸收养分，促进发育成长，并有促进乳腺发育、增生乳汁的功效；青木瓜又能促进消化，消除肉食积滞、改善小腹腰臀脂肪堆积，也能调节血压，改善血液品质，搭配富含蛋白质的肉类，可丰胸美乳、润肤美颜、抗衰老。

32 木瓜排骨汤

——润肤美颜，丰胸美乳

薏苡仁冬瓜排骨汤

——美白净斑，改善虚胖浮肿

材料：

薏苡仁1杯（电饭锅量杯），冬瓜375克，排骨300克

调味料：

盐1小匙

●适合对象：一般人皆宜，唯孕妇不宜，体质十分虚寒的人少食用。

做法：

1. 排骨放入滚水中汆烫，捞起洗净沥干。
2. 薏苡仁洗净沥干。冬瓜削皮去籽，洗净切块。
3. 排骨、薏苡仁、冬瓜放入锅中，加2000毫升水以大火煮沸，转小火继续炖30分钟。
4. 加调味料即成。

薏苡仁能美白肌肤、淡化黑斑、抚平扁平疣，同时能活化经络、去湿气、利尿，让肌肤富有弹性。薏苡仁含醇类、糖类，能增强免疫功能、降低血糖、抑制细胞癌变，还能兴奋子宫增添情趣，但有滑胎之虞，孕妇不宜，搭配具清热利尿、消肿的冬瓜一同煮食，能使肢节更灵活，改善虚胖浮肿，塑身效果更为明显。

材料：

乌鸡爪6只，香菇8～10朵，姜1块

调味料：

盐1小匙

● 适合对象：人人皆宜，特别是中年妇女、老年人或男性皆可经常食用。

做法：

1. 鸡爪剁除趾尖，每只剁成两段洗净。
2. 香菇泡软拧干，去蒂头切半。姜洗净，切片。
3. 鸡爪、香菇、姜放入锅中，加1500毫升水以大火煮沸，转小火继续炖30分钟。
4. 加调味料即成。

鸡爪含丰富的胶质，提供胶原蛋白，是凝结细胞防御力、抗氧化的重要物质。香菇是能提升免疫力的食物，促进干扰素产生，增强抗病力与免疫功能。凤爪香菇汤能防止细胞被破坏，产生癌变，且能增强肌肤抵御力，有对抗自由基、紫外线和空气污染伤害等功效。

34 凤爪香菇汤

——增强皮肤抵御紫外线和污染能力

材料：牛腩600克，马铃薯1个，胡萝卜1根，洋葱1个，番茄1个

调味料：红酒200毫升，酱油3大匙，盐1/2小匙，糖1/2大匙

做法：

1. 牛腩洗净切块。马铃薯、胡萝卜削皮洗净，切块。
2. 洋葱去外膜洗净，切块。番茄洗净去蒂头，切块。
3. 牛腩、马铃薯、胡萝卜、洋葱、番茄放入锅中，加酱油、盐、糖和1000毫升水，以大火煮沸，转小火继续炖30分钟。
4. 加入红酒继续炖5分钟即成。

红酒炖牛肉

——红润脸色，增加肌肤弹力

35

●适合对象：人人皆宜，气血循环不佳、手脚冰冷、容易疲惫、嗜睡及肌肤干涩者可多食用。

材料：南瓜600克，虾仁225克，胡萝卜1根

调味料：盐1/2小匙，西洋芹香料少许

做法：

1. 南瓜削皮去籽，洗净切块。胡萝卜削皮洗净。
2. 南瓜、胡萝卜放入锅中，加800毫升水煮熟，倒入果汁机打成泥状。
3. 倒入锅中以中火煮沸，加入虾仁煮熟，放盐调味，撒上西洋芹香料即成。

南瓜鲜虾浓汤

——抗衰老，祛除老年斑

36

●适合对象：人人皆宜，特别是中老年人，或是衰老速度快过年龄增长速度者都可将其作为家常养生汤。

材料：哈什蚂（雪蛤）1只，罐头白果1罐，
　　　枸杞8克

调味料：冰糖100克

做法：

1. 哈什蚂（雪蛤）自腹部剪开，取出哈什蚂（雪蛤）油以清水泡发，挑去杂质沥干。
2. 煮锅中加1200毫升水，以大火煮沸，放入哈什蚂（雪蛤）、白果、枸杞煮沸，转中小火继续煮3分钟。
3. 加冰糖调味即成。

●适合对象：人人皆宜，特别是更年期妇女、生殖系统虚弱或是切除子宫的人适合常食用。

37

雪蛤白果甜汤
——柔肤除纹，缓和更年期症状

白及绿豆薏苡仁汤
——抚平伤口，祛斑不留疤

38

材料：绿豆1/2杯，薏苡仁1/2杯
药材：白及8克
调味料：冰糖100克

做法：

1. 绿豆、薏苡仁洗净放入锅中，加入白及、1200毫升水以大火煮沸，转小火继续煮30分钟。
2. 加冰糖煮溶即成。

●适合对象：一般人皆宜，特别是好长青春痘、皮肤过敏的人更适合食用。

材料：蹄筋300克，绞肉150克，青菜1棵
药材：炒杜仲20克
调味料：盐1小匙，胡椒粉少许
做法：

1. 蹄筋放入滚水中氽烫，捞起洗净。绞肉加1/2小匙盐和胡椒粉拌匀。
2. 炒杜仲放入锅中，加1200毫升水以大火煮沸，转小火继续煮15分钟，再转大火，放入蹄筋继续煮5分钟；以汤匙臼肉馅成丸状，加入汤中煮熟。
3. 青菜洗净切段，放入汤中，加盐调味即成。

● 适合对象：人人皆宜，女性、孕妇、产妇可经常食用。

杜仲蹄筋肉丸汤
——预防皮炎，润肤柔发

材料：山药150克，新鲜海菜40克，绞肉150克
调味料：盐1小匙，胡椒粉少许，淀粉1小匙
做法：

1. 山药削皮洗净，切丁。
2. 绞肉加1/2小匙盐，淀粉和胡椒粉拌匀。
3. 锅中加1000毫升水，放入山药丁，以大火煮沸，转小火继续煮10分钟。
4. 用汤匙臼绞肉成丸状放入汤中，以中大火煮熟，加海菜煮沸，放盐调味即成。

● 适合对象：人人皆宜，唯消化不良、宿积不化、胃肠积滞的人少食用。

山药海菜肉丸汤
——燃烧脂肪，排除宿便

PART5

强身益寿，养生保健

现代人的生活模式，不外是应酬频繁、杂务多、饮食不正常、睡不够、压力大、收入少、运动量不足……；放眼望去这些都是不利于身心健康的生活习惯。享受健康必须排除这些障碍，并有效规划个人的生活习性。平时除了常运动、好学习、调整规律的生活步调之外，改变饮食方法最值得尝试，因为食物可以提供维持生命的要素和能量，巩固身体的基本架构，促进细胞代谢与循环，增强抗病力，提升免疫功能，强身益寿、保健身心。

冬虫夏草炖鸭汤

——止咳平喘，调补肾气

材料： 鸭肉600克

药材： 冬虫夏草10克

调味料： 盐1小匙，米酒30毫升

做法：

1. 鸭肉放入滚水中氽烫，捞起洗净。

2. 冬虫夏虫冲净，挑出杂质。

3. 鸭肉、冬虫夏草放入锅中，加1500毫升水以大火煮沸，
转小火继续炖40分钟。

4. 加盐调味，洒入米酒即成。

● 适合对象：性功能失调，久咳成痨、肺痨、抵抗力差或常受流感之苦的人适宜多食用。

冬虫夏草炖鸭汤是调养久咳虚喘、阳痿遗精、肺痨血痰的重要汤品。**冬虫夏草能扩张支气管平滑肌，有促进肾上腺素分泌的作用，能达到止咳平喘化痰的效果；能增强吞噬细胞的活力，提高抗体活性，促进淋巴T细胞的转化，增进免疫功能，使机体强壮，补益肾气，改善阳痿遗精、腰膝酸痛、性功能早衰症状，对妇女月经失调也有疗效。

材料：

酒酿1/2碗，鸡腿1只，枸杞8克

调味料：

盐1小匙

●适合对象：男女老少皆宜，四肢冰冷，脸色苍白，瘦弱乏力者可常食用。

做法：

1. 鸡腿剁块，放入滚水中氽烫，捞起洗净，加1200毫升水以大火煮沸，转小火继续炖25分钟。

2. 加入酒酿、枸杞继续煮5分钟，加调味料即成。

酒酿是糯米和酒曲酿制而成的酵米，能益气活血、生津液，搭配鸡腿和枸杞，能补充丰富的养分，促进血液和经脉循环，维护新陈代谢正常，适量食用，能调和气血，改善末梢血液循环，提高生理活性，提高抗病力。

42 酒酿鸡腿汤

——改善末梢血液循环，提高抗病力

材料：鸡腿1只

药材：生参1棵，枸杞8克

调味料：盐1小匙，米酒30毫升

做法：

1. 鸡腿剁块，放入滚水中汆烫，捞起洗净。
2. 鸡腿、生参、枸杞放入锅中，加1500毫升水以大火煮沸，转小火继续炖25分钟。
3. 加盐调味，洒入米酒即成。

人参鸡汤
——增强抗病力，减缓衰老速度

●适合对象：人人皆宜，特别是新陈代谢缓慢、抵抗力弱者宜常食，唯高血压、肥胖者、体质热实的人慎食。

材料：鸡腿1只

药材：当归8克，熟地黄8克，白芍8克，川芎4克，党参8克，茯苓8克，白术8克，甘草4克，枸杞8克，大枣8枚

调味料：米酒30毫升

做法：

1. 鸡腿剁块，放入滚水中汆烫，捞起洗净。
2. 全部药材、鸡腿，加1500毫升水以大火煮沸，转小火继续炖30分钟，洒入米酒即成。

八珍鸡汤
——调理气血循环，促进新陈代谢

●适合对象：适合大众食用，月经失调、慢性出血、虚弱且面无血色的人适宜以其为辅助食疗，在季节转换由秋入冬之际宜用此汤进补。

材料：鸡腿2只，老姜1块、麻油1/2碗

调味料：米酒300毫升

做法：

1. 鸡腿剁块洗净，拭干。老姜洗净拭干，拍裂切片。

2. 炒锅加麻油，放入姜片以中小火爆至微焦。

3. 加入鸡腿炒匀，倒入米酒、1000毫升水以大火煮沸，转小火继续炖15分钟即成。

●适合对象：最适合产妇及体质虚寒的人食用，一般人也适宜冬日搭食，可提高抗寒力。

45

麻油鸡汤

——补虚强身，快速恢复体能

参须鲍鱼排骨汤

——祛寒暖身，聪耳明目

46

材料：鲍鱼600克，排骨375克

药材：参须20克，枸杞10克

调味料：盐1小匙

做法：

1. 排骨放入滚水中汆烫，捞起洗净。

2. 参须以清水浸泡5分钟，挑去杂质。鲍鱼刷净，沥干。

3. 排骨、参须放入锅中，加1500毫升水以大火煮沸，转小火继续炖30分钟。

4. 放入枸杞、鲍鱼煮熟，加调味料即成。

●适合对象：一般人皆宜，老年人或更年期妇女可常食用；但鲍鱼不容易消化，若只喝汤汁，养生效果一样好。

47

材料：芡实1杯（电饭锅量杯），鸭胗3个

调味料：盐1小匙

做法：

1. 鸭胗洗净切片。芡实洗净沥干。
2. 芡实放入锅中，加1200毫升水以大火煮沸，转小火继续炖30分钟。
3. 放入鸭胗以中火煮沸，转小火继续炖5分钟，加盐调味即成。

芡实鸭胗汤
——增强体质，改善虚弱

●适合对象：一般人皆宜，特别是性能力不全或是老年尿失禁者可常食，有妇科病困扰的人也可多食。

材料：鲫鱼2尾，胡萝卜1段，葱1棵

药材：当归8克，何首乌8克

调味料：盐1/2小匙

做法：

1. 胡萝卜削皮洗净，切片。葱去根须，洗净切段。
2. 鲫鱼洗净拭干，放入油锅中以中火炸至两面酥黄，捞起。
3. 当归、何首乌放入锅中，加1200毫升水以大火煮沸，转小火继续炖15分钟。
4. 放入鲫鱼、胡萝卜继续炖10分钟，加葱、盐调味即成。

●适合对象：一般人皆宜，产妇缺乳、身体浮肿、体弱又关节痛的人可多食用。

首乌当归鲫鱼汤
——保肝抗菌，强健筋骨

48

材料：苹果1/2个，菠萝1/6个，木瓜1/4个，猕猴桃1个，龙眼8粒、樱桃2枚

调味料：冰糖50克

做法：

1. 苹果、木瓜削皮洗净，去籽切丁。猕猴桃削皮洗净，切丁。菠萝削皮去心，切块。龙眼剥壳，去籽。
2. 将所有材料(樱桃除外)放入锅中，加600毫升水煮沸，放入冰糖煮溶即成。
3. 倒入容器，放上樱桃即可食用。

●适合对象：适合一般人食用，但胃肠虚寒、胃酸分泌失调或有溃疡者不宜食用。

49

五色水果甜汤

——滋补五脏，改善免疫力

木瓜炖奶

——润肤养颜，美化曲线

50

材料：木瓜1个，鲜奶200毫升

调味料：冰糖30克

做法：

1. 木瓜洗净擦干，横剖去籽。
2. 取一半木瓜，用挖球状的器具，挖成一球状，放入另一半木瓜内，加入冰糖、鲜奶，放入碗盅。
3. 移入电饭锅，外锅加1杯水炖熟即成。

●适合对象：人人皆宜，特别是便秘时，皮肤干涩，发育不良者可常食用，但胃肠虚寒，经常腹泻，或有乳糖不耐受症者不宜食用。

PART6

舒眠解压，疏筋活血

睡一夜好觉是当代人的奢望，尤其对三餐或生活步调不正常的人来说更是如此。现代人普遍有吃太多、动太少的困扰，尤其是压力大、竞争激烈之际，难免以吃来代偿及舒解压力，但是以这种方式未必能消除压力，反而容易造成胃肠负担、营养过剩、气血不通、循环滞碍、体型肥胖等症状。建议你应该从选择健康食材及调配饮食着手，再强化"三多"原则：多运动、多喝水、多爱自己，令气血调和、筋骨舒展，维持理想体重与身材；更要懂得爱惜自己，调节生活步调，取得睡眠休息与工作打拼的平衡点。

材料：鸡腿1只

药材：当归8克，熟地黄8克，白芍8克，川芎4克，大
　　　枣8枚，枸杞4克

调味料：盐1小匙，米酒30毫升

●适合对象：贫血、血虚的人可常食用，一般人也可食用，能辅助血液循环，唯月经量多，食少大便稀薄、脾胃虚弱消化不良的人不宜食用。

做法：

1. 鸡腿剁块，放入滚水中汆烫，捞起洗净。
2. 鸡腿、全部药材放入锅中，加1500毫升水
   以大火煮沸，转小火继续炖25分钟。
3. 起锅前加盐调味，洒入米酒即成。

四物鸡汤是调理妇科病的代表方，能补血调经、行气止痛，改善月经失调、经闭腹痛、胎产不顺、面色萎黄、皮肤粗涩，并顺肝气、祛除跌打损伤淤痛、润肠、止血，缓解血虚、便秘。虽是妇科主方，但不含雌激素，亦适合男性食用。有益精填髓效果，对遗精盗汗、腰膝酸软、须发早白、头晕眼花、风湿痹痛有效，使男性雄风再现。此汤品更能提高淋巴细胞的转化率，可抗维生素E缺乏症，增强身体抵抗力。

51 四物鸡汤

——补血调经，行气止痛

52 归芪鸡翅汤

——调理气血，增强免疫力

材料：鸡翅4只

药材：当归10克，黄芪20克，大枣6枚

调味料：盐1小匙

做法：

1. 鸡翅剁成两段，放入滚水中汆烫，捞起洗净。
2. 鸡翅、全部药材放入锅中，加1200毫升水以大火煮沸，转小火继续炖20分钟。
3. 加盐调味即成。

●适合对象：最适合贫血、虚弱、脸色苍白的人，大量失血后尤其适合实时进食。

当归配黄芪补气又补血，擅长调理气血两虚，如贫血、白细胞减少、大量失血后体弱，以及妇女经血量过多造成的眩晕、产后血虚、发烧等都适合食用此汤品以补中益气、活血养血；同时还具有抗衰老、抑菌、促进伤口愈合、保肝、增强免疫力的功能。

材料：鸡腿1只
药材：田七4克，红花4克
调味料：盐1小匙

●适合对象：跌打损伤、产后恶露不下、淤血阻滞、有淤痛或伤痛者都适合，唯孕妇不宜食用。

做法：

1. 鸡腿剁块，放入滚水中氽烫，捞起洗净。

2. 鸡腿、田七放入锅中，加1200毫升水以大火煮沸，转小火继续炖25分钟。

3. 撒入红花继续煮3分钟，加盐调味即成。

田七又名三七，可活血行淤，止淤滞疼痛、跌打伤痛，行气通经络效果佳；也能止血、调节血压和心跳频率；红花能活血通经，止关节酸痛、疮痈肿痛。此汤品能活络血行、舒展筋骨、疏通脉络，但活血通经之际，也有收缩子宫的作用，孕妇避免食用。

53 田七红花鸡汤

——活血祛淤，舒展筋骨

54 烧酒鸡

——改善畏寒及手足冰冷

材料：

鸡腿1只

药材：

当归8克，黄芪10克，桂枝8克，丁香4克，大枣6枚

调味料：

米酒1000毫升

●适合对象：末梢循环不畅、体质虚寒、怕冷，长期待在空调环境或喜欢吃冰品的人可经常食用。

做法：

1. 鸡腿剁块，放入滚水中余烫，捞起洗净。

2. 鸡腿、全部药材放入锅中，加米酒，以大火煮沸，转小火继续炖20分钟即成。

当归加黄芪最利于调理气血，改善衰弱倦怠、月经失调症状；桂枝善于祛风寒、治感冒，打通经脉；丁香能温肾助阳、温胃散寒、止呃逆呕吐。食用此汤品有活化细胞的代谢功能、提升免疫功能、改善畏寒、手足冰冷、润泽脸色、减轻疲劳的功效。

材料：排骨300克，莲藕2节，胡萝卜1段

药材：干荷叶1叶

调味料：盐1小匙，白醋1大匙

做法：

1. 排骨放入滚水中氽烫，捞起洗净。

2. 荷叶剪成6厘米，洗净放入滚水中氽烫，捞起沥干。

3. 胡萝卜削皮洗净，切片。莲藕削皮洗净，切块。

4. 排骨、莲藕、胡萝卜、荷叶放入锅中，加1500毫升水、白醋以大火煮沸，转小火继续炖30分钟，加盐调味即成。

荷叶含有莲咸、酮A类，能防衰老、抗癌，提升抵抗力，清热消暑、除烦解闷、生津止渴效果佳，并可调节血压，防治各种血液病；莲藕能提供多种营养，提高免疫力和抗病力，也能防治多种出血症。常食用荷叶莲藕排骨汤能清心消暑、祛热除烦，有避免异常出血的作用。

55 荷叶莲藕排骨汤

——预防出血，减少淤青

材料：鲢鱼头1个，甜玉米1支，胡萝卜1段，大白菜225克，菜豆75克，金针菇75克，纱布袋1个

药材：柏子仁8克，酸枣仁8克

调味料：盐1小匙

做法：

1. 甜玉米洗净切段。胡萝卜削皮洗净，切片。菜豆洗净。大白菜洗净剥大片。金针菇去根洗净。
2. 鲢鱼头洗净拭干，放入油锅中以中小火炸至两面酥黄，捞起。
3. 柏子仁、酸枣仁放入纱布袋绑紧。
4. 鱼头、全部材料、药袋放入砂锅中，加水盖满材料，以中火煮沸，转小火煮约20分钟，加盐调味即成。

双仁鱼头汤
——安心养神，镇静催眠

材料：猪脑1个，青江菜1棵

药材：枸杞8克

调味料：盐1/2小匙

做法：

1. 猪脑以牙签挑去薄膜和血丝，洗净沥干，放入碗盅加水盖满材料，撒上枸杞，隔水蒸20分钟。
2. 青江菜去朽叶，洗净切段，汆烫后放入汤中，加盐调味即可起锅。

枸杞猪脑盅
——安神助眠，改善记忆力衰退

材料：桂圆110克，新鲜百合球2个
调味料：红糖50克

做法：

1. 百合剥瓣，修掉老边，洗净沥干。桂圆剥散。
2. 百合、桂圆放入锅，加1000毫升水以大火煮沸，转小火继续煮5分钟。
3. 加红糖继续煮3分钟即成。

●适合对象：容易烦躁或莫名兴奋者，失眠、善忘、常觉得全身虚乏、常处于紧张状态的人都适合多食用；一般人也可食用，有助于调节压力，消除紧张、助安眠。

桂圆百合甜汤

——缓解焦躁忧郁，提高睡眠品质

芋头八宝粥

——改善体虚，舒压助眠

材料：芋头75克，莲子75克，红豆75克，绿豆75克，紫米75克，薏苡仁75克，麦角75克，大红豆75克
调味料：红糖100克

做法：

1. 芋头削皮洗净，切丁。全部材料洗净。
2. 全部材料加1800毫升水以大火煮沸，转小火继续煮25分钟（每隔7~8分钟轻轻搅拌以免沾锅）。
3. 加入红糖拌匀，继续煮5分钟即成。

●适合对象：人人皆宜，唯不宜一次多量食用，以免肠胃饱胀；胀气严重者建议少食。

60 红糟羊肉汤
——改善贫血，预防眩晕

材料：羊肉片600克，老姜1块
调味料：红糟1/2碗，盐适量，糖1小匙

做法：

1. 老姜刷净，切段拍裂。
2. 放入油锅中，先下姜爆至微焦，加入红糟、糖炒香。
3. 加入1000毫升水，转中大火煮滚，放入羊肉片煮熟，加盐调味即成。

●适合对象：一般人都适合，尤其是血虚瘦弱、产后虚劳、男性阳气不足者；唯体壮热燥、身体强壮的人不适宜。

羊肉及老姜是祛寒暖胃、益肾补阳的佳品，其甘温的特性能温补气血、开胃助食、强魄健体、改善虚弱疲劳、贫血症状，可预防眩晕、腰膝酸软；也适合为坐月子补养的汤品，产后虚冷、腰酸、腹痛、食欲差的人都适合，也能温暖肾气和子宫，提高受孕几率。

PART7

健胃整肠，帮助消化

　　均衡摄取营养是维护健康的基本功，对于各种维生素和矿物质，身体所需量虽不多，但每个都是关键也不可或缺，加上蛋白质、脂肪、碳水化合物、水等营养素共同和谐运作，才能有效维持机体正常代谢，提高免疫力。若想让胃肠消化、吸收功能维持正常，一定要调整饮食习惯，改变不良习性，以减少毒素的产生，进而强化胃肠功能、预防慢性疾病发生。

61 鲜菇竹笋鸡汤

——帮助胃肠蠕动，清肠消积

材料：

鸡腿1只，新鲜香菇5朵，绿竹笋300克

调味料：

盐1小匙

●适合对象：一般人皆宜，但胃肠虚弱或有溃疡病史的人慎食，因为竹笋的纤维质会造成胃肠不适；如服用中药或大病初愈，避免食用竹笋，因其甘性偏寒，有碍药气行走及吸收。

做法：

1. 鸡腿剁块，放入滚水中氽烫，捞起洗净。
2. 香菇洗净去蒂头，十字对切成4片。绿竹笋剥壳，修去老硬部分，洗净切块。
3. 鸡腿、香菇、绿竹笋放入锅中，加1500毫升水以大火煮沸，转小火继续炖30分钟，加盐调味即成。

香菇含菇多糖，有助T淋巴细胞作用，能益胃气、开胃、助食欲，促进干扰素产生，增强抗病力；绿竹笋富含膳食纤维，可清肠消积。鲜菇竹笋鸡汤能帮助胃肠蠕动，快速排出体内废物和毒素，增强免疫功能。

材料：猪肚1只

药材：芡实75克，山药20克，茯苓20克，薏苡仁40克

调味料：盐1小匙，米酒适量

●适合对象：一般人皆适合，特别是汗尿不畅、手足浮肿、消化不良、胃口不佳者；唯薏苡仁性滑，常吃容易导致流产，孕妇不宜食用。

做法：

1.猪肚剔除肥油，放入滚水中汆烫，捞起洗净，切长条。

2.猪肚、全部药材放入锅中，加1800毫升水。

3.移入电饭锅，外锅加3杯水，待炖熟后继续焖20分钟加盐调味，进食前滴数滴米酒即可食用。

猪肚能补虚损、健脾胃；芡实能补脾止泻、益肾固精，改善频尿症状；山药能补肾涩精、润肺、健脾胃、调理妇女更年期症状、预防衰老；茯苓、薏苡仁能利尿消肿，去除体内湿气。经常食用四神猪肚汤，可有健脾益胃、促进食欲、利尿消肿、强健胃肠、促进生长发育的功效。

62 四神猪肚汤

——健脾益胃，促进生长发育

63

芦笋魔芋排骨汤

——调整胃肠消化吸收，节制摄食量

材料：芦笋300克，魔芋150克，排骨300克

调味料：盐1小匙

做法：

1. 排骨放入滚水中余烫，捞起洗净。魔芋洗净，切斜纹再切块。

2. 芦笋修去老皮和粗硬部分，洗净切段。

3. 排骨、魔芋放入锅中，加1500毫升水以大火煮沸，转小火继续炖25分钟。

4. 加入芦笋继续炖5分钟，放盐调味即成。

●适合对象：一般人皆宜，特别适合便秘、体重过重、容易增胖、食量较大者食用，唯芦笋含有嘌呤成分，痛风者不宜食用。

芦笋高纤、低脂、零胆固醇，又富含维生素A、维生素B族和维生素C，能促进新陈代谢、增加体力、养颜美容、抗老防衰、降低致癌率、调整胃肠消化吸收、消脂瘦身、预防高血压。魔芋低卡高纤，能大量吸收水分而产生饱足感，协助胃肠蠕动，预防便秘，促使毒素排出。常食用此汤有控制食量、节制油脂摄取、保健胃肠，辅助新陈代谢的功效。

材料：排骨375克，菠萝225克

药材：山楂15克

调味料：盐1小匙

●适合对象：嗜食肉、不喜欢吃含纤维质蔬果及食量大、运动量少者适合多食用，唯胃液分泌异常，胃肠溃疡患者应慎食。

做法：

1. 排骨放入滚水中余烫，捞起洗净。菠萝削皮，切块。

2. 菠萝、排骨、山楂放入锅中，加1500毫升水以大火煮沸，转小火继续炖25分钟。

3. 加盐调味即成。

山楂能增加胃液消化酶，可消除脂肪积滞；菠萝含有助于分解蛋白质及肉类的酶，故能缓解胃肠胀满，搭配排骨可促进人体对蛋白质的吸收与利用。山楂菠萝子排汤消脂祛热量效果佳，还可扩张血管，增加血流量、降低血压和胆固醇及保护心血管健康，唯其消化力强，空腹时不宜一次多量食用。

64 山楂菠萝子排汤
——帮助消化，促进蛋白质吸收与利用

65

椒粒莲子猪肠汤
——温胃祛寒，促进食欲

材料：猪肠600克

药材：胡椒粒8克，莲子150克，大枣8枚

调味料：盐1小匙

做法：

1. 猪肠剔除肥油，放入滚水中汆烫，捞起洗净，切段。

2. 莲子、大枣、猪肠、胡椒粒放入锅中，加2000毫升水以大火煮沸，转小火继续炖40分钟，加盐调味即成。

●适合对象：胃肠虚弱、消化吸收不良、食欲差及嗜食冷饮冰品者适合多食用，唯溃疡者胡椒量不宜太多，容易刺激胃黏膜引起充血性发炎。

猪肠能补虚损、健脾胃，对饮食失调、食欲不振、胃肠蠕动失调有效，胡椒含有胡椒碱、挥发油等成分，适量摄取能温胃祛寒，缓和胃寒、呕吐、腹痛、腹泻症状；莲子亦能健胃整肠、止泻。椒粒莲子猪肠汤能健胃整肠，改善消化吸收功能，缓解腹泻，增进食欲。

材料：
排骨300克，芥菜300克，姜1块
调味料：
盐1小匙

做法：

1. 排骨放入滚水中氽烫，捞起洗净。姜洗净，切片。

2. 芥菜剥开洗净，放入滚水中氽烫，捞起冲冷水，切大片。

3. 排骨、芥菜、姜片放入锅中，加1500毫升水以大火煮沸，再转小火继续炖20分钟，加盐调味即成。

芥菜有长年菜之称，提供丰富维生素、矿物质及膳食纤维，能协助胃肠蠕动、清理体内废物；其特有的辣味能刺激消化器官、增加摄食量，搭配排骨煮食可提供优质蛋白质，促使芥菜丰富的脂溶性维生素A被充分消化吸收，有助抗体产生并有保护视力的功效。

66 芥菜排骨汤

——协助胃肠蠕动，清理体内废物

材料：牛蒡300克，胡萝卜1根，鸡翅3只
调味料：盐1/2小匙
做法：

1. 鸡翅剁小段，放入滚水中氽烫，捞起洗净。

2. 牛蒡削皮洗净，切滚刀块，下锅前先浸于淡盐水。胡萝卜削皮洗净，切块。

3. 牛蒡、胡萝卜、鸡翅放入锅中，加1200毫升水以大火煮沸，再转小火继续炖20分钟，加盐调味即成。

●适合对象：人人皆宜，肥胖、胆固醇高、血糖高者可常吃，孕妇及产妇要多摄食，可帮助胎儿脑部发育。

牛蒡胡萝卜鸡翅汤
——防肠内寄生虫孳生，排出体内废物

材料：萝卜375克，胡萝卜1根，鱼丸300克
药材：山楂20克
调味料：盐1小匙
做法：

1. 萝卜、胡萝卜削皮洗净，切块。

2. 萝卜、胡萝卜、山楂放入锅中，加1500毫升水以大火煮沸，转小火继续煮25分钟。

3. 加入鱼丸，转中火煮熟，加盐调味即成。

●适合对象：高血压、胆固醇高、消化不良或常吃油腻食物的人更适合；一般人偶尔食用能维持胃肠正常运作的功能。

山楂萝卜鱼丸汤
——调理腹胃闷痛，消化不良

材料：鸡蛋1个

药材：肉桂粉1/4小匙

调味料：味霖1小匙

做法：

1. 煮锅加350毫升水煮滚，打入鸡蛋，转中火煮至蛋白凝固，蛋黄软嫩。

2. 加入味霖，撒上肉桂粉待凉，放入冰箱冷藏20分钟即可食用。

●适合对象：一般人皆宜，但生蛋黄不宜用来喂食婴幼儿；胃肠极为虚弱、习惯性腹泻、胃肠过敏者慎食。

69

肉桂温泉蛋

——预防胃寒及腹痛

马蹄蛋花汤

——清胃肠热燥，利尿降火

70

材料：荸荠150克，鸡蛋1个

调味料：冰糖30克

做法：

1. 荸荠洗净削皮，切细。鸡蛋打匀成汁。

2. 荸荠放入锅中，加800毫升水，以大火煮沸，再转小火继续煮10分钟。

3. 放入蛋汁，加冰糖调味搅匀即成。

●适合对象：热性体质、容易上火、情绪起伏大、呼吸粗重而声大者极适合食用，唯口唇无色、脸色苍白、两眉泛青、四肢冰冷、畏寒怕冷者不宜食用。

PART8

预防伤风感冒

　　感冒分为二型，一型为普通感冒，例如着凉、受风邪；另一型为受流感所传染，原因都不外乎抵抗力弱，自愈力低落。如何增强呼吸道抵抗病菌或病毒的能力，最重要的是强化体质，增强免疫系统功能，减弱病菌对人体的侵袭，降低过敏物质在体内的影响力。但是要如何提高抗病力呢？运动是累积健康、提高免疫力的不二法门，运动能促进新陈代谢，激发机能的活力，以增进体能，强化肌力，若再搭配均衡的营养与适当的休闲活动，则能维持免疫细胞的正常功能，促进抗体产生，维持呼吸道健康。

材料：鸡腿1只

药材：西洋参片20克，枸杞8克

调味料：盐1小匙

●适合对象：肺热咳嗽严重或痰中有血丝者尤其适合；但体质虚寒、气弱力乏、食欲不振者不宜食用。

做法：

1. 鸡腿剁块，放入滚水中氽烫，捞起洗净。
2. 鸡腿、西洋参片放入锅中，加1500毫升水以大火煮沸，再转小火继续炖20分钟。
3. 加入枸杞继续炖5分钟，加盐调味即成。

西洋参含有人参皂甙、人参醇类、多糖类、果胶、蛋白质、氨基酸及微量元素等有效成分，维持人体正常生理机能，增强抗病力，延缓器官组织衰退老化。西洋参炖鸡汤滋补效用平和缓进，更能被人体充分吸收利用，发挥补肺益气、清热退烧、止肺热喘咳的效果。

71 西洋参炖鸡汤

——补肺益气，清热退火

72 沙麦山药鸡汤
——维持鼻，喉及肺黏膜的健康

材料：鸡腿1只

药材：沙参10克，麦冬10克，山药150克，大枣8枚

调味料：盐1小匙

做法：

1. 鸡腿剁块，放入滚水中汆烫，捞起洗净。

2. 山药削皮洗净，切块。

3. 鸡腿及全部药材放入锅中，加1500毫升水以大火煮沸，转小火继续炖25分钟，加盐调味即成。

●适合对象：适合体热、热型感冒者食用，唯肺寒咳嗽、痰稀淡、腹泻者慎用。

沙参、麦冬能润肺止咳、生津止渴、清心除烦，是改善呼吸器官虚弱、虚火旺盛而咳嗽的重要药物，所含有效成分可刺激支气管黏膜，使分泌物增加，发挥祛痰止咳、改善口干舌燥的作用。沙麦山药鸡汤能维持鼻、喉及肺黏膜的健康，增加呼吸性感染的抵抗力、清心助眠、缓解便秘、增进食欲、滋补体能。

材料：

鱼片300克，嫩姜1块，新鲜紫苏叶3片

调味料：盐1/2小匙，米酒适量

●适合对象：感冒初患而畏寒、不出汗、头痛、低温发烧者适宜多食用；在季节转换如秋季转冬季时，多吃可防范感冒、风寒。

做法：

1. 姜洗净切丝。紫苏叶洗净切丝。
2. 煮锅中加1000毫升水以大火煮沸，放入姜丝、鱼片，转中火煮至鱼肉熟嫩。
3. 放入紫苏叶，滴少许米酒，加盐调味即成。

紫苏叶含有挥发油，能刺激汗腺分泌，有退烧解热、祛散寒气、改善风邪感冒引起的畏寒、呕吐、头痛、肢节酸痛、肩颈僵硬、胸闷喘息的作用；也能刺激循环与代谢，改善脾胃气滞、胀满而引起疼痛，促进消化液分泌，增加胃肠蠕动，预防便秘，缓解鱼虾蟹引起的食物中毒非常有效。

73 紫苏鱼片汤

——退烧解热，缓和感冒症状

74

罗汉果杏仁猪肺汤

——避免风寒感冒，改善喘咳痰多

材料：猪肺300克，葱1棵

药材：罗汉果1个，杏仁10克

调味料：盐1小匙

做法：

1. 猪肺洗净，放入滚水中汆烫，捞起洗净，切片。罗汉果洗净敲碎。葱洗净切丝。

2. 罗汉果、杏仁放入锅中，加1200毫升水以大火煮沸，再转小火继续煮20分钟。

3. 加入肺片，转中火续煮5分钟，加葱丝、盐调味即成。

●适合对象：播音族、发声族都适合，可提高肺活量，美化嗓音；长期在密闭空间或空气不洁，或弥漫刺激性气味环境中，如美发师、油漆工作、装潢师都适合常食。

罗汉果益肺气、润咽喉、祛咳化痰，改善嗓音沙哑症状；杏仁能调理肺气、止咳平喘，改善喘咳痰多、胸满闷胀症状，也能润肠通便；猪肺补肺气，止咳嗽。此汤品能提升呼吸系统抵抗流感能力及过滤污染物质，避免经常性风寒感冒或是过敏性呼吸道炎，并能润喉，改善嗓音。

材料：

洋葱1个，羊肉2片

调味料：

盐1/2小匙

●适合对象：人人皆宜，特别是抵抗力弱，容易疲劳、常腹泻、消化不良的人更适宜多食用。

做法：

1. 洋葱去膜洗净，切丝。羊肉切细丝。

2. 热油锅，加入羊肉炒酥，放入洋葱丝炒至微焦。

3. 加800毫升水以大火煮沸，转小火慢熬至洋葱熟软，加盐调味即成。

洋葱独特的辛辣味来自于有挥发性的硫化丙烯，会刺激神经传导，顺畅血液循环，促进新陈代谢及清新耳目和口鼻，并具发汗、解热的功效，可缓解感冒初期症状、化痰止咳、改善手脚冰冷，红润肤色。而洋葱煮熟后食用可增强体力，消除疲劳。洋葱也是抗氧化剂，预防各种癌症发生，尤其能有效抵抗胃癌，同时也是保护心血管健康的优良蔬菜。

75 洋葱汤

——化痰止咳，改善手脚冰冷

材料：梨1个
药材：川贝母8克，大枣5枚
做法：

1. 梨削皮洗净，去核籽切块。
2. 梨、川贝母、大枣放入碗盅，加水盖满材料，以保鲜膜封住盅口。
3. 移入电饭锅，外锅加2杯水，食物炖熟后，续焖5分钟即成。

贝母炖梨

——防治支气管炎，润肺消痰

76

●适合对象：风热感冒、痰浓黄、声音沙哑、重咳发烧者宜食用，发声族、播音族、教师族都适合将其作为平日保养嗓音的辅助品；唯体弱肺虚、冷咳痰稀白者不宜食用。

材料：梨1个，嫩姜1块
调味料：冰糖30克
做法：

1. 梨削皮洗净，去核籽，切块。嫩姜洗净，切斜片。
2. 梨、嫩姜及冰糖放入碗盅，加水盖满材料，以保鲜膜封住盅口。
3. 移入电饭锅，外锅加1/2杯水，食物炖熟后，续焖5分钟即成。

●适合对象：发音族群用来调理嗓音最适合，感冒初期也可食用，唯感冒严重或感冒症状为虚弱乏力、痰稀白、舌苔淡白者不宜食用。

生姜冰糖炖梨

——清润喉咙，预防胸闷不畅

77

材料：白木耳8克，莲子150克

药材：大枣8枚

调味料：冰糖80克

做法：

1. 白木耳浸清水泡软，去硬梗切小朵。莲子洗净，沥干。

2. 白木耳、莲子、大枣放入锅中，加1200毫升水以大火煮沸，再转小火继续煮30分钟，加冰糖调味即成。

●适合对象：一般人皆宜，平日可作为养肺汤品，一次不宜大量食用，排便稀软者也要慎食；如果是风寒咳嗽也不宜食用。

银耳莲枣甜汤

——缓解失眠头晕，咽干口燥

杏仁露

——止咳定喘，滑肠通便

材料：杏仁粉50克，杏仁豆腐1块

调味料：蜂蜜10克

做法：

1. 杏仁豆腐切小块。

2. 杏仁粉放入容器，倒入350毫升冷开水拌匀，加入蜂蜜搅拌（亦可冲热开水，调泡成热饮）。

3. 加入杏仁豆腐即成。

●适合对象：久咳不愈、肠燥便秘者最宜，皮肤粗糙干燥、提早衰老者亦可常食用；唯习惯性腹泻或虚咳痰稀白的人不宜食用。

80 葱豉豆腐汤

——排汗祛寒，清热消炎

材料：

豆腐1盒，葱2棵，淡豆豉1大匙

调味料：

盐1/2小匙

做法：

1. 葱去根须洗净，切葱花。豆腐切块。
2. 煮锅加800毫升水，以大火煮沸，放入豆豉、豆腐煮熟。
3. 撒上葱花，加盐调味即成。

●适合对象：感冒风寒致心浮气躁、懊恼难眠者尤其适合。平日配食则能增进呼吸道健康，并调节汗腺分泌功能。

豆豉搭配葱来应用，可解伤风感冒、轻度发烧、畏寒怕冷、头晕头痛的现象，也可缓和烦躁不安、胸闷胀满、懊恼不眠、纳食失调症状。当感冒初患，自觉有上述症状时，即刻以豆豉加葱煮食，趁热食用让汗排出能祛寒、止头痛、退烧，但要立即更换汗湿衣物，并避免直接吹风，能有效减轻症状，甚至痊愈。搭配豆腐煮食，更有清热消炎、降温助食的作用。

PART9

调节性功能，
预防骨质疏松

　　步入30岁正值壮年期，身体机能逐日往下坡走，骨质密度的改变即是最好的例子，如果日常摄食磷、钙、维生素 D 等营养不足，又喜欢喝咖啡、碳酸类饮料，运动量也不足，又不爱接受阳光洗礼，也许30岁即已衰老到50岁的骨质。尤其是步入更年期，激素分泌情况有所改变，女性会面临骨质疏松的威胁，而男性虽无此方面的困惑，但性功能的调节则是一大课题。建议平时多注意饮食均衡，常做运动，排解压力，安排有益身心的休闲娱乐活动，相信对健康会有很大的助益。

81 麻油鸡脬汤

——提高性欲和受孕率

材料：
鸡脬150克，老姜1块，麻油2大匙
调味料：
米酒100毫升

做法：

1. 鸡脬放入滚水中氽烫，捞起沥干。老姜洗净，切片。

2. 炒锅加麻油，放入姜片以中火爆至微焦。

3. 倒入米酒、300毫升水，以大火煮沸，加入鸡脬煮沸即成。

●适合对象：一般人都宜适量摄食，特别是男性在青春期或步入中年性功能渐走下坡者都宜多食。

鸡脬富含蛋白质和激素，有助激素的产生，增加性活力，一般认为男性尤其需要。所含蛋白质能促进神经传导，提高身体的灵敏度和增强肌肉组织，搭配富含苯胺基丙酸的麻油，能辅助性器官成熟，提高性欲和受孕几率，有助于不孕症的治疗与康复。

材料：鸡腿1只，黑豆150克
药材：炒杜仲20克，巴戟天10克，大枣6枚
调味料：盐1小匙，米酒适量

●适合对象：一般男女皆宜，孕妇亦适合；唯体质燥热或血压低者不宜大量进食。

做法：

1. 鸡腿剁块，放入滚水中汆烫，捞起洗净。黑豆洗净。

2. 鸡腿、黑豆、杜仲、巴戟天、大枣放入锅中，加1500毫升水以大火煮沸，转小火继续炖30分钟。

3. 起锅前加盐调味，滴入米酒即成。

杜仲、巴戟天、黑豆能补肾阳、强筋骨，改善风湿酸痛、筋骨痿软、骨质疏松、月经不调、小腹冷痛、子宫循环虚弱难受孕、阳痿、腰酸痛等现象，并能促进T淋巴细胞转换，活化免疫功能。食用此汤品能强筋健骨、调理性机能、避免早衰、延年益寿，还有降压、利尿、镇痛及顺养胎气的作用。

82 杜戟黑豆炖鸡汤
——调理性机能，强筋健骨

83 栗子龙骨汤

——添精益髓，健骨益齿

材料：

栗子300克，猪脊椎骨375克，胡萝卜1根

调味料：

盐1小匙

●适合对象：人人皆宜，特别是妇女步入更年期，或男性自觉体力渐衰、腿脚渐乏都可多食用。

做法：

1. 猪脊椎骨放入滚水中氽烫，捞起洗净。

2. 栗子放入滚水中氽烫，捞起去膜、洗净。胡萝卜削皮洗净，切块。

3. 栗子、猪脊椎骨、胡萝卜放入锅中，加1500毫升水以大火煮沸，转小火继续炖30分钟，加盐调味即成。

猪脊椎骨又称龙骨，能添精益髓、茁壮骨骼、预防软骨病，搭配栗子能益气和胃、健脾补肾，改善腰酸背痛、脚膝酸软等症状，还能提供多种营养素，促进人体对钙、磷、镁、铁等成分的吸收。栗子龙骨汤能使骨骼和牙齿坚固，心血管维持健康，延缓衰老的速度，避免骨密度快速下降。

材料：乌鸡爪225克，猪尾巴225克，带膜花生150克

调味料：盐1小匙

●适合对象：人人皆宜，尤其是处于发育期的青少年、产妇、更年期妇女更可作为养生辅食的汤品。

做法：

1.猪尾巴剁段，鸡爪去趾尖、剁成两大段，放入滚水氽烫，捞起洗净。

2.花生洗净，放入滚水中氽烫，捞起洗净。

3.乌鸡爪、猪尾巴、花生放入锅中，加1600毫升水，以大火煮沸，转小火继续炖30分钟，加盐调味即成。

花生被视为是"植物肉"，富含不饱和脂肪酸、维生素 E 等成分，能延缓细胞老化、减轻疲劳、预防肌肉变性、生殖功能发生障碍；也富含钙质，可预防软骨症、骨质疏松症。带膜花生其膜衣能抗纤维蛋白溶解，促进骨髓制造血小板、加强毛细血管收缩，维持血管弹性，搭配乌鸡爪、猪尾等富含胶原蛋白的食材，能改善营养吸收不良、发育缓慢、脾胃失调等症状，有助成长、预防骨质疏松或软化，并有润肤养颜、减少皱纹及增生乳汁的功效。

84 凤爪猪尾花生汤

——预防软骨症，骨质疏松症

85 蘑菇浓汤
—— 强健骨骼，防治蛀牙

材料：
蘑菇75克，鲜奶300毫升，奶油1大匙
调味料：
盐1/2小匙，荷兰芹末少许

做法：
1. 蘑菇洗净，去蒂头，切片。
2. 奶油入锅融化，加入蘑菇片炒软。
3. 加入鲜奶，以小火煮沸（边煮边搅拌，以免沾锅）。
4. 加盐调味，撒上荷兰芹末即可食用。

●适合对象：人人皆宜，无论成长痛、初经腹痛、老年骨质疏松、蛀牙者都可常食、多食。

蘑菇含多糖类，能调节白细胞减少症、慢性肝炎，并具抗癌作用；鲜奶含钙质、维生素D，是强健骨骼、牙齿最重要的营养成分，能防治佝偻、蛀牙、软骨及老年性骨质疏松；此外，钙质也具缓和失眠、减轻经期腹痛、成长痛或少女月经初潮疼痛等症。

材料：
丁香鱼干75克，番茄2个，大白菜300克，海带结75克
调味料：
盐1/2小匙

●适合对象：任何年龄层都适宜，唯有小孩要注意鱼刺。

做法：

1. 番茄底部划十字，放入滚水中汆烫至皮翻起，捞起去皮、切块。

2. 大白菜剥叶洗净，切段。海带结洗净。

3. 全部材料放入锅中，加1200毫升水以大火煮沸，再转小火继续煮25分钟，加盐调味即成。

鱼类是良好的动物性蛋白质来源，是构成白细胞和抗体的主要成分，多吃鱼类能维护基本的防御能力。丁香鱼能提供丰富的钙、磷，促进脑细胞生长，并可强筋健骨、巩固牙齿、预防蛀牙。食用此汤品不仅能促进骨骼生长发育，更具抗老防衰、美容养颜、抚平细纹、维持肢体灵活的作用。

86 鱼干蔬菜汤
——抗老防衰，强筋健骨

材料：鱿鱼3片，蟹足肉3条，虾仁3尾，鱼
肉2片，蛤蜊2枚，奶油1大匙，面粉
1大匙，鲜奶350毫升

调味料：盐1/2小匙，黑胡椒粉粒少许

做法：

1. 鱿鱼、蟹足肉、虾仁、鱼肉洗净沥干。
蛤蜊浸泡淡盐水，吐沙洗净，捞起沥干。

2. 奶油入锅融化，加入面粉以小火炒糊，
倒入鲜奶搅匀，以中小火煮沸。

3. 放入全部海鲜煮熟，加盐调味，撒上黑
胡椒粉粒即成。

● 适合对象：人人皆宜，
特别是发育期青少年男女
可多食用；唯体质极虚
弱、对海鲜过敏或消化
不良者不宜。

海鲜浓汤

——舒筋活血，预防骨质增生

87

材料：猪软骨225克，发芽米(发了芽的糙
米)1杯（电饭锅量杯），虾米适量

调味料：盐1/2小匙

做法：

1. 猪软骨放入滚水中氽烫，捞起洗净。

2. 虾米以清水泡5分钟，挑去杂质，沥干。发
芽米洗净。

3. 发芽米、猪软骨、虾米放入锅中，加1000
毫升水以大火煮沸，转小火继续煮30分钟，
加盐调味即成。

● 适合对象：人人皆适
合，平日即可与白米饭交
换食用。

软骨炖发芽米

——活化关节，抗氧化

88

材料：地瓜300克，姜1块

调味料：红糖100克

做法：

1. 地瓜削皮洗净，切滚刀块。姜洗净，切片。
2. 姜、地瓜放入锅中，加水盖满材料，以大火煮沸，再转小火继续煮20分钟。
3. 加入红糖续煮5分钟即成。

●适合对象：人人皆宜，唯营养过剩或进行减肥、胃肠容易胀气的人少吃。

89

红糖姜片地瓜汤

——强健骨骼，增加骨密度

坚果奶汤

——预防发育迟缓，帮助长高

90

材料：鲜奶350毫升，即溶麦片30克、核桃1大匙，松子1/2大匙，南瓜子1/2大匙，葡萄干1/2大匙，腰果1大匙

调味料：果糖1/2大匙

做法：

1. 核桃、腰果、松子、南瓜子拍裂。鲜奶倒入煮锅，放入即溶麦片，以中小火煮沸。
2. 加入果糖拌匀，起锅加入各种坚果和葡萄干即成。

●适合对象：人人皆宜，无论发育期、成长期、孕期、更年期、老年期都适宜。

PART10

抗病防癌，
强化生命机能

　　维持生命的能量，常取决于食物的摄取。众多食材各有其营养效益和性能作用，对抗病防癌方面来说，应该多吃抑制氧化速度、延缓衰老、抗癌变、防肿瘤、削减自由基的食材，如富含维生素 A、维生素 C、维生素 E 的甜椒、马铃薯、花椰菜等；更重要的是要积极地坚守"三少"守则：少吃油脂、少吃甜食、少碰烟酒，即可防止免疫细胞遭受破坏，自然可以强身健体，防癌防肿瘤，快速提高抗病力与免疫功能，也能有效防御病毒的侵蚀。

材料：田鸡3只，大蒜10瓣

调味料：盐1/2小匙，米酒适量

● 适合对象：人人皆宜，抵抗力弱者可常食用。

做法：

1. 大蒜剥皮洗净。田鸡切块，放入滚水中氽烫，捞起洗净。

2. 大蒜加1000毫升水以大火煮沸，转小火继续煮10分钟。

3. 加入田鸡，转中大火煮沸，加盐调味，滴入米酒提味即成。

大蒜含大蒜辣素，有杀菌和抑菌效果，并促进 T 淋巴细胞转化，增加白细胞及巨噬细胞的活性，加强抗病力，提高免疫功能，还有健胃、镇静、强身的功效，对防治感冒和肠道细菌性感染有效，临床医学也证实，多食大蒜料理能防治胃癌、肠癌。田鸡能滋阴清热、利水消肿，富含蛋白质、多种矿物质和维生素，但脂肪少，常食用不仅不会增加热量，而且可弥补大蒜防治病变的效果。

91 大蒜田鸡汤

——预防肠道细菌感染，防治胃肠癌

92

半枝莲蛇舌草鸡汤

——灭菌抗炎，抗肿瘤

材料：鸡腿1只

药材：半枝莲10克，白花蛇舌草10克，枸杞8克，大枣6枚

调味料：盐1小匙

● 适合对象：可作为治癌辅助汤品或为化学放射性治疗后辅助食品，可减轻副作用。

做法：

1. 半枝莲、白花蛇舌草放入锅中，加1800毫升水以大火煮沸，转小火继续熬15分钟，过滤汤汁。

2. 鸡腿剁块，放入滚水中汆烫，捞起洗净。

3. 鸡腿、大枣放入汤汁，以大火煮沸，转小火继续炖25分钟。

4. 加入枸杞续炖5分钟，加盐调味即成。

半枝莲含黄酮类、酚性成分的抗癌物质，能清热解毒，消肿疮疡，防治肺癌、胃肠道癌，利尿消肿；蛇舌草含醇类、有机酸，能刺激细胞吞吐能力。半枝莲蛇舌草鸡汤能促进抗体形成，具有灭菌、抗炎、抗肿瘤、防癌的功效。

材料：鳗鱼1尾

药材：参须20克，枸杞8克

调味料：盐1/2小匙，米酒10毫升

●适合对象：尤其适合青壮年、青春期、成熟期及老年期适量食用。

做法：

1. 鳗鱼去鳃、肠腹，洗净切段。参须浸泡5分钟，沥干。

2. 鳗鱼、参须、枸杞放入碗盅，加水盖满材料，以保鲜膜封住盅口。

3. 移入电饭锅中，外锅加2杯水，待食物炖熟后，加调味料即成。

枸杞参须鳗鱼汤是增添阳刚、强化男性体能的代表方，可提高白细胞数量、抗肿瘤，滋补肝肾，益精明目，调节血糖，降低胆固醇，阻止动脉硬化，同时能促进生殖系统成熟，增强免疫力，使视力、听力维持正常状态，提升脑力，也是保肝肾、防癌的好汤。

93 枸杞参须鳗鱼汤

——保肝肾，抗肿瘤

94

鹿茸枸杞鲜虾汤

——预防细胞质变

材料：鲜虾600克

药材：鹿茸8克，枸杞8克

调味料：盐1/2小匙，米酒30毫升

做法：

1. 鲜虾去须脚，挑肠泥，洗净。

2. 鹿茸、枸杞放入锅中，加1000毫升水以大火煮沸，转小火熬10分钟。

3. 加入鲜虾，转中大火煮熟，加调味料即成。

●适合对象：男女虚弱、肾气不足、老年日益体衰、房事过勤者可多食用。

鹿茸能大力补充肾阳、益精养血、强筋健骨，有明显促进成长发育、兴奋机体功能、预防性功能失调的作用。鹿茸枸杞鲜虾汤含有激素、胶质、蛋白质、钙质等成分，对细胞的健康与凝结力大有助益，不但能促进血红细胞增生，亦能预防细胞质变。

材料：羊肉600克，生姜1块

药材：党参10克，当归8克，枸杞4克，黑枣6枚

调味料：盐1/2小匙，米酒30毫升

●适合对象：人人皆宜，特别是瘦弱乏力，体虚气不足者；唯体热肥壮型者少食用。

做法：

1. 羊肉放入滚水中汆烫，捞起洗净。生姜洗净，切片。
2. 羊肉、生姜、全部药材放入锅中，加1800毫升水，以大火煮沸，转小火继续炖45分钟。
3. 加入盐、米酒调味即成。

羊肉炉是冬令进补的重要汤品，能增强体能、强健骨骼，提高身心的灵敏度与防御指数，促进气血循环、发肤柔嫩，改善瘦弱体虚、脸色苍白、唇甲黯灰症状，还能促进激素分泌、增加精子数量、提高受孕率，使体内专门制造能量的脂肪酸被正常利用，充实体能，消除疲劳，集中注意力。

95 羊肉炉

——增强体能，改善瘦弱体虚

●适合对象：人人皆宜，适合各种年龄层，不分性别皆宜。

材料：绞肉300克，绿花椰菜225克，马铃薯1个，胡萝卜1段，淀粉1大匙

调味料：盐1小匙

做法：

1. 绞肉加1/2小匙盐拌匀，以手抓肉馅来回掷甩至肉馅富有弹性，取适量握成丸状，表层抹上一层淀粉。
2. 放入油锅以中小火炸至表面呈金黄色，捞起即成狮子头。
3. 绿花椰菜切小朵，撕去梗皮，洗净。马铃薯削皮洗净，切块。胡萝卜削皮洗净，切片。
4. 马铃薯、胡萝卜放入锅中，加1300毫升水以大火煮沸，转中小火，放入狮子头续煮20分钟。
5. 加入绿花椰菜煮沸，加盐调味即成。

花椰狮子头汤

——调节免疫力，抗氧化

材料：马铃薯1个，番茄1个，红甜椒1个，节瓜1条，猪肋骨300克

调味料：盐1/2小匙

做法：

1. 猪肋骨放入滚水中氽烫，捞起洗净。
2. 马铃薯削皮洗净，切块。番茄洗净，切块。红甜椒切半，去籽蒂洗净，切块。节瓜去蒂洗净，切块。
3. 全部材料放入锅中，加1500毫升水以大火煮沸，转小火继续炖30分钟，加盐调味即成。

● 适合对象：一般人皆适合，特别是发育中青年人群及老年人群应经常食用。

薯椒肋骨汤

——抗癌防流感，延年益寿

材料：黑芝麻粉50克，无花果2个

调味料：红糖30克

做法：

1. 无花果切小块。
2. 煮锅倒入350毫升水煮沸转小火，放入芝麻粉拌匀，加红糖调味。
3. 放入无花果即可食用。

●适合对象：老少咸宜，唯严重腹泻、体重过重、营养过剩者少食。

98

无花果芝麻糊

——延长细胞寿命，预防神经障碍

绿茶丸子甜汤

——排除毒素，促进新陈代谢

99

材料：绿茶粉20克，小汤圆75克

调味料：冰糖30克

做法：

1. 煮锅加500毫升水以大火煮沸，加入汤圆煮至浮出水面。
2. 加入冰糖拌匀，倒入绿茶粉即成。

●适合对象：一般人皆宜，唯脑神经衰弱、失眠多梦者不宜；消化不良者亦少食，以免因食用汤圆而导致气滞腹胀。

100

金线莲胡鲶汤

——协助肝脏解毒排毒，增强免疫力

材料：胡鲶375克，姜1段
药材：金线莲10克
调味料：盐1/2小匙

做法：

1. 胡鲶洗净，放入滚水中氽烫，捞起切段。姜洗净，切片。

2. 金线莲放入锅中，加1500毫升水以大火煮沸，转小火继续熬15分钟，过滤汤汁。

3. 加入胡鲶、姜片，转中大火续煮20分钟，加盐调味即成。

●适合对象：人人皆宜，体虚气弱者可常食。

金线莲能抗菌、防癌、消除体内不正常细胞，协助肝脏解毒排毒；胡鲶是药补的重要食材，能提供优质蛋白质、胶质、脂肪、维生素、微量元素等成分。金线莲土虱汤能增强人体抗病毒的能力、促进生长，也是强身健体的好汤品。

BUILDING JEWISH LIFE

Sukkot & Simhat Torah

by Joel Lurie Grishaver

photographs by Jane Golub,
Joel Lurie Grishaver and Alan Rowe
additional photography by Bill Aron

illustrated by Joel Lurie Grishaver
additional line art by Linda Nusbaum

**Torah Aura Productions
Los Angeles, California**

For Our fathers Paul, Jack, and Ira—
our model builders of Jewish life.

Thank You:
Temple Ner Tamid, Rancho Palos Verdes
Temple Emanuel, Beverly Hills
Steven, Frieda, Daniel & Shira Huberman
Mayer Schames
Bruce, Tamar & Rami Raff
Bruce, Debby, Rachel, Naomi & Jonathan Powell
Ron & Michael Wolfson
Melton Research Center

Our Advisory Committee:
Melanie Berman, Sherry Bissel-Blumberg, Gail Dorph,
Paul Flexner, Carolyn Starman-Hessel, Freda Huberman,
Ben Zion Kogen, Debi Mahrer, Fran Pearlman, Peninnah
Schram, Joyce Seglin.

Our contributors
photographs on pages 6, 14, and 15 © Bill Aron
Text, photographs and line art on pages 23-28 taken from
Being Torah, © Torah Aura Productions
illustrations for *Our First Sukkah* © Linda Nusbaum

Our Professional Services:
copyeditor: Carolyn Moore-Mooso
Alef Type & Design
Alan's Custom Lab
Gibbons Color Lab
Delta Lithograph

Library of Congress Cataloging-in-Publication Data
Grishaver, Joel Lurie.
   Building Jewish Life — Sukkot and Simhat Torah
   Summary: Explores the history, significance, and
customs of the Jewish holidays, Sukkot and Simhat Torah..
   1. Sukkot — Juvenile literature.   2. Simhat
Torah — Juvenile literature.   [1. Sukkot. 2. Simhat
Torah.   3. Holidays.   4. Fasts and feasts — Judaism]   I.
Title.
BM695.S8G74   1987   296.4'33   87-16190
ISBN 0-933873-13-1 (pbk.)

Torah Aura Productions
4423 Fruitland Avenue
Los Angeles, California 90058

Manufactured in the United States of America.

PART ONE: THINGS WE DO ON SUKKOT

This is a *sukkah*[1]. When you look through the roof of a sukkah, you can see the sky. At night you can see the stars.

A sukkah is a hut which Jews build for the holiday of *Sukkot*. On Sukkot, it is a *mitzvah*[2] to eat, drink and sleep out in the sukkah.

The sukkah is almost like a time machine. When we spend time in the sukkah, we are taken back to things which happened a long time ago.

Footnotes are found on page 46

Once, the Jews were slaves in Egypt. With God's help, they escaped. It took them forty years to walk from Egypt to the land of Israel. The Jews spent a long time in the wilderness. They spent many, many nights sleeping out in sukkot.

When we build a sukkah, we feel a little bit like the Jews who escaped from Pharaoh. We remember how bad it is for any person to be a slave—and how good it is to live in freedom.

God could have taken the Jewish people out of Egypt and brought them right to Israel. Instead, God made them spend forty years camping out in the wilderness.

One Jewish teacher explained:

If God had brought the Jewish people right to Israel, every family would have become busy with its own orchards, fields and vineyards. For forty years, the Jewish people had to work together. They had to share the water and make sure that everyone had enough. They also had to make sure to gather enough food for everyone. And, they had to live in sukkot.

For forty years, the Jewish people worked together, helped each other, and became a people. They also had forty years to study the Torah. *Tanhuma, B'shalah*

5

The Torah makes spending time in the sukkah a mitzvah "so that Jews will know that God had the Children of Israel live in sukkot when they were brought out of the land of Egypt." *Leviticus 23.42-43*

When we leave our homes and sleep out in the sukkah, we are just like the Jews who lived in sukkot in the wilderness. We remember how the Children of Israel became a nation.

Bill Aron

6

When Joshua led the Jewish people into the Land of Israel,
they quickly became farmers. Jews spread out all over the land.
Each family had its own fields to work. Every fall they went out into
fields to gather the harvest. Because some of the fields were far
from their homes, they often built sukkot to live in while they
gathered the harvest.

When we eat out in our sukkah, we remember to give thanks
to God for helping all food to grow.

7

The Torah is filled with laws and stories which helped them get ready for living in the Land of Israel. It made the Children of Israel into a special people.

The Torah taught Jewish farmers that they had to share the food which they raised with the poor, the widow and the orphan.

Pe'ah [3] means corner. Jewish farmers had to leave the corners of their fields for those who needed food. The poor and the hungry could come and harvest their own food. *Leviticus 23.22.*

She'kheha [3] means forgotten. If a Jewish farmer forgot a bundle of grain or a bunch of vegetables in the field, the farmer could not go back for them. Once forgotten, they had to be left for people who were hungry to come and gather. *Deuteronomy 24.19.*

Leket [3] means something which has been dropped. When a farmer was gathering the harvest, any food which was dropped also had to be left for people who were not able to grow their own food. *Leviticus 19.9.*

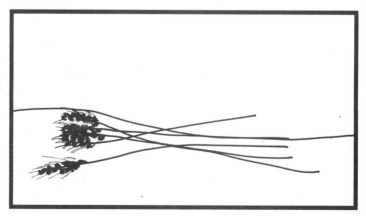

Today, Jews decorate their sukkot with fruits and vegetables. We hang strings of popcorn and cranberries. A sukkah looks like a harvest. When we eat out in the sukkah, we are taken back to the days when every Jew was a farmer. The sukkah reminds us to give thanks to God who helps every living and growing thing. It also teaches us that the best way to be thankful is to remember the mitzvot which teach us to share with those who are in need.

King Solomon was the son of King David. He built a big beautiful Temple on the top of a mountain in Jerusalem. The Temple was the place where Jews came to give thanks to God. Jews from all over came to Jerusalem.

Three times a year, Jews left their homes and brought the best of their harvests to the Temple. Three times a year, on *Sukkot*, *Pesaḥ* and *Shavuot*, Jews went up by foot to Jerusalem.

Many of the Jews who came to Jerusalem spent the week-long holiday living in sukkot.

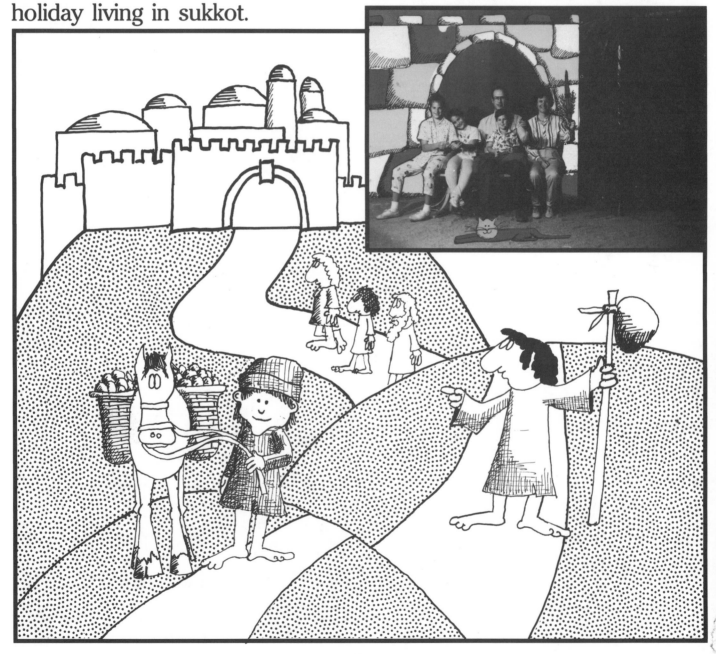

In the days when all Jews came to the Temple in Jerusalem, Sukkot was the biggest and most important holiday in the Jewish year. Sukkot lasts for a whole week, and in those days, Sukkot was a week-long party. There was music and dancing. They made bonfires and burned the old underwear of the *kohanim*, the family which worked in the Temple. Stories are even told about how some of the rabbis used to juggle torches.

When we celebrate in the sukkah, we are taken back to those celebrations when all Jews came to Jerusalem.

When the Pilgrims came to America in 1620, they felt just like the Children of Israel. They, too, had come to a new land to find freedom. The Bible was a very important part of their lives. Their first year in America was very hard. When their first harvest was completed, they wanted to have a party to thank God for helping them survive. They read in the Torah about the harvest feast called sukkot. They believed that they should also give thanks to God for helping them. They called their American celebration of Sukkot "Thanksgiving."

Today, we still make Sukkot into a week-long celebration. We eat and drink in the sukkah. We even do something called *ushpizin*[4]. Ushpizin is inviting famous Jews from history to join us in the sukkah.

The ushpizin invitation list includes: Abraham, Sarah, Isaac, Rebekkah, Jacob, Rachel, Leah, Joseph, Moses, Miriam, Aaron, Hannah, David and Esther.

The sukkah is like a time machine. When we sit in it, we are taken back to many things which happened long ago.

This is a *lulav*. It is made up of 1 **palm** branch, 2 **willow** branches and 3 branches of **myrtle**.

In the Torah, we are taught:

"On the first day of Sukkot, you should take the **etrog**, and branches of the **palm**, **willow**, and **myrtle**—and celebrate before God."

We use the *etrog* and the *lulav* to perform this mitzvah.

Bill Aron

This is an etrog. It is a citrus fruit sort of like a lemon.

The *etrog* and *lulav* are a mystery. The Torah makes them a mitzvah, but doesn't explain why.

One teacher explained:

The *etrog* and *lulav* are like a person. The **palm** looks like a backbone. The **myrtle** leaves look like eyes. The **willow** leaves look like a mouth. And, the **etrog** looks like the heart. The lesson is that we are supposed to thank God with our whole body.

Another teacher explained:

Bill Aron

Just as there are four kinds of plants, so there are four kinds of Jews.

The **willow** has no taste and cannot be smelled. It is like the Jew who learns no Torah and who does no good deeds.

The **myrtle** branch can be smelled, but has no taste. This is like the Jew who knows little Torah, but who still does many good deeds.

The **palm** branch has a taste but no smell. This is like the Jew who knows much Torah, but who does not do good deeds.

The **etrog** can be both tasted and smelled. This is like the Jew who both knows much Torah and does good deeds.

The *etrog* and *lulav* help us remember that a good Jew both learns about what is right by studying Torah and works hard to find chances to help others.

A third teacher explained:

These four different kinds of plants show us that God helps all kinds of plants to grow.

PART TWO: SHEMINI ATZERET

At the end of the week of Sukkot there is another holiday called *Shemini Atzeret.*

To understand Shemini Atzeret, you have to know about *Eretz Yisrael*, the land of Israel. In Israel, it only rains during the winter. It will never rain during the summer, spring or fall. That means that all the rain that farmers need must fall during the winter.

Shemini Atzeret comes just before the beginning of the winter rains. It is the holiday on which we begin to ask God for rain in our daily prayers.

This is a *Torah*. Torah means "teaching." The Torah is a handwritten scroll which contains the Five Books of Moses.

The Torah teaches us stories and laws. It tells the story of how God chose the Jewish people to teach the rest of the world how to be righteous. It teaches us how to lead a good Jewish life.

Jews read part of the Torah every week. We start at the beginning and finish the whole Torah in a year. As soon as we are finished, we start all over again.

*S*imhat Torah is the day on which we read the last words in the Torah. It is also the day on which we start over by reading the first words again. For Jews, the Torah is a never-ending book.

A *simḥa* is a happy occasion. It is a special time like a birthday, a bar or bat mitzvah, a wedding or the birth of a baby. It is a time to give a party.

Simḥat Torah is the day set aside in the Jewish year to make a special occasion for the Torah. We give the Torah a party. There is singing and dancing. We wave flags. We even have a Torah Parade.

19

On Simḥat Torah we take out all of the Torah scrolls and march around the synagogue seven times. We call each parade a *hakafah*.

The Torah is something which belongs to every Jew. On Simḥat Torah everyone can dance with the Torah, carry it, touch it, and feel close.

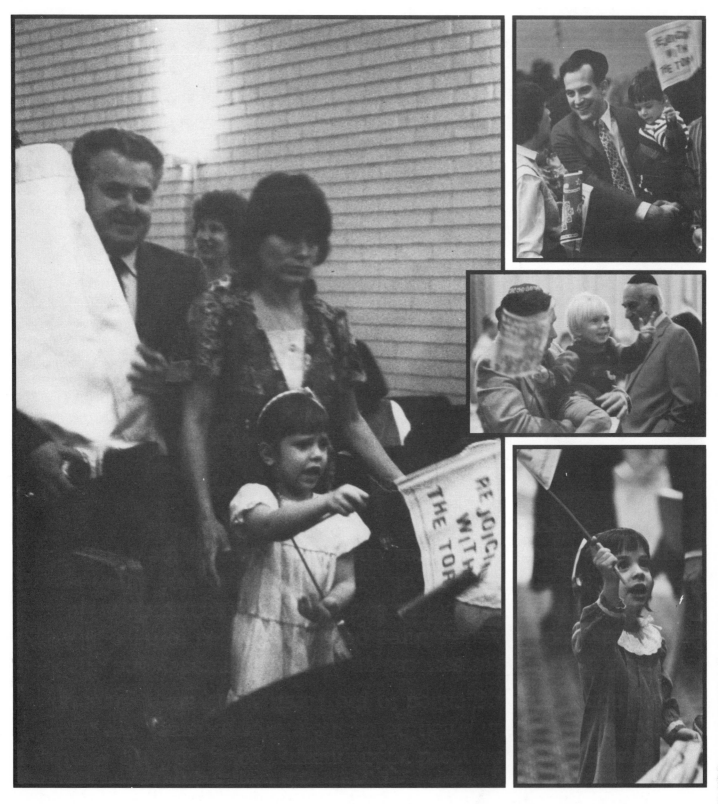

*A*liyah is a Hebrew word which means "going up." We say that a person makes aliyah when he or she moves to Israel. We also call the honor of being called to the Torah an aliyah, a going up.

Jews read the Torah at services on Monday, Thursday and Shabbat. On Monday and Thursday, three people are called to have aliyot. They chant the *brakhot* before and after the Torah reading. On Shabbat, there are seven aliyot. On Simḥat Torah, one aliyah is given to the children. It is their chance to go up to the Torah, just like adults do every week.

After every Torah reading, two more people are given aliyot called *hagbahah* and *g'lilah*. To do hagbahah a person must be very strong. Hagbahah is sort of like weight lifting. The person who does hagbahah lifts the Torah high over his or her head so that everyone can see it. Torah is for every Jew. The person who does g'lilah helps to roll and dress the Torah.

The Last Story in the Torah

After forty years of camping in the wilderness, the Jewish people are ready to enter the land of Israel. They are camped just across the Jordan river. The Torah ends with the story of the last time that Moses and God talk together.

Moses went up to Mount Nebo,
top of the Pisgah (which is across from Jericho).

The LORD showed him all the **land** of Israel.
From Gilead to Dan, all of Naphtali,
the **land** of Ephraim and Manasseh.
From all the **land** of Judah to the Mediterranean Sea.
The Negev. From the Plain of Jericho to Zohar.

The LORD said to him:
"This is the **land** which I promised
to Abraham, to Isaac, and to Jacob.
saying: 'To your future family I will give it.'

I let you see it with your own eyes.
But you will not cross into it."

23

Moses, the Lord's servant, died there,
in the **land** of Moab,
by the Lord's word.

The LORD buried him in the valley
of the **land** of Moab,
and no person knows his grave to
this day.

Never again will Israel have a
prophet like Moses,
who knew the LORD face to face.
Who did all the signs and wonders
which God sent him to do
in the **land** of Egypt.
To Pharaoh
and all his workers
and all his **land**.

And all the mighty hand
and all the wonders
which Moses made happen
before the eyes of all Israel.

Discuss:
1. *Share everything you know about Moses. Why was he the greatest prophet ever?*
2. *If you could talk to God, face to face, what would you ask?*

The First Story in The Torah

The first story in the Torah tells us how God created the universe. It is a story of "Beginnings." We learn how everything began. Especially, we learn about how God made people in God's own image.

Beginnings:
God **created** the heavens and the earth.
The earth was unformed.
Darkness was over the deep.
The breath of God was over the waters.

God said: "Let there be light."
And there was light.
God said: "**GOOD**."
God called the light: "Day."
God called the darkness: "Night."

There was evening.
There was morning.
Day one.

God said: "Let there be a space between the waters." And God made the space. God called the space: "Sky."

There was evening.
There was morning.
A second day.

God said: "Let dry land appear."
And it was so.
God called the dry land: "Earth."
God called the waters: "Sea."
God said: "**GOOD**."

God said: "Let plants and green things grow."
And it was so.
God said: "**GOOD**."

There was evening.
There was morning.
A third day.

God said: "Let there be lights in the sky.
They will be signs for the seasons, for the days and for the years."
And it was so.
God made two great lights.
One light to shine during the day.
One light to shine at night, and the stars, too.
God placed them in the sky, to give light on the earth and to divide between light and darkness.
God said: "**GOOD**."

There was evening.
There was morning.
A fourth day.

God said: "Let the waters swim with life.
And let the sky be filled with birds."
And God created the great sea-serpents,
and the crawling things which filled the waters,
and the birds, too.
God said: "**GOOD**."

God blessed them: "Be fruitful and become many and fill the waters and the sky."

There was evening.
There was morning.
A fifth day.

God said: "Let there be wildlife on the earth."
God made the wildlife.
There were beasts and creeping things.
God said: "**GOOD**."

God said: "Let Us make people in Our image.
Let them rule over the fish and the birds,
over the beasts and the creeping things."
God made people in God's image.
God created people—both man and woman.

God blessed them:
"Be fruitful
and become many,
and fill the earth
and master it."

God saw everything God had made.
God said: "Very **GOOD**."

There was evening.
There was morning.
The sixth day.

The heavens and the earth were finished.
God finished all the work on the seventh day.
On the seventh day God rested from all the work.

God blessed the seventh day and made it holy,
because on it God rested from all the work.
Everything had been **created**.

Finding A Torah Lesson

A. Count how many times the word **land** is used in **The Last Story in the Torah**. ———————— times.

Count how many times the word **GOOD** is used in **The First Story in the Torah**. ———————— times.

B. When the Torah wants us to teach an important lesson, it repeats one word many times.

C. In **The Last Story in the Torah**, the word ———————— is used 8 times.

This teaches us that God gave the Jewish people the promised ———————— of Israel.

D. In **The First Story in the Torah**, the word ———————— is used 7 times.

This teaches us that everything which God created is ———————— .

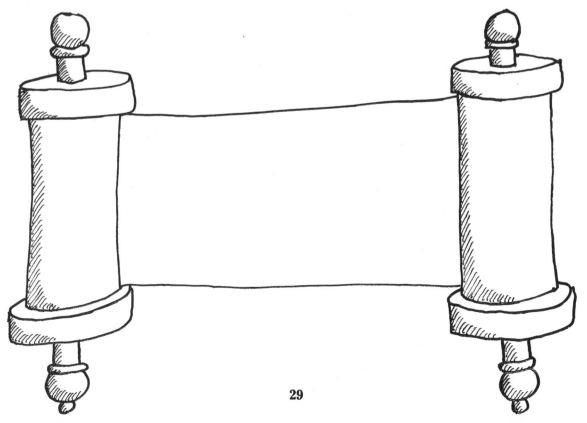

Sukkot In The Wilderness

Imagine that you were in a sukkah in the wilderness with Moses. Draw a picture of what you can see through the front door.

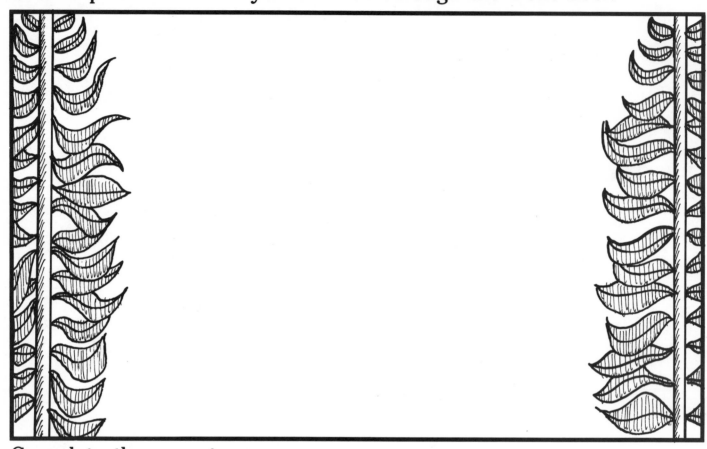

Complete these sentences:
1. Once, the Jewish people were slaves in _____.
2. God brought them out.
3. They spent _____ years in the wilderness.

4. They lived in_____.
5. Every morning except Shabbat, they went out to gather manna.
6. Manna was food which God made fall from the sky.
7. They also had to make sure that everyone had enough_____.
8. In the wilderness, Moses taught _____ to the people.

Torah

sukkot

Egypt

water

forty

Sukkot In The Fields

Imagine that it was a long, long time ago and you were a Jewish farmer in Israel. You are living in a sukkah and harvesting your field. Draw a picture of what you can see through your sukkah roof.

Complete these sentences:

1. When the Jewish people entered the Land of
   _____, they became farmers.
2. Often the fields were very far away from their houses.
3. During _____ time they sometimes camped out in sukkot.
4. When they gathered their crops, they had to leave the _____ for the widow, the stranger, and the orphan.
5. They also had to leave anything they _____ or had _____.
6. It is a mitzvah to share what we have with those who are in need.

corners

harvest

dropped

Israel

forgotten

31

A Home Harvest

Read and discuss this story:

The Torah told Jewish farmers to share part of their harvest with the homeless and the hungry. They had to leave the corners of their fields, anything they dropped and anything they had forgotten.

Hundreds of years later, a rabbi named Tanhum lived in a city named Tiberias. He didn't have a farm. He studied the rules for farmers and decided to share his harvest in his own way. He shared his harvest every time he went shopping. When he only needed one piece of meat, he would buy two. When he only needed one bunch of vegetables, he would buy two. One was for the poor and one was for himself.

Today, hundreds of years later, a group of Jews in Dallas, Texas, read the story of rabbi Tanhum. They decided to learn from his story. They asked everyone in their community to "get the tzedakah habit." They asked everyone to buy an extra can of food every time they went to the supermarket.

The mitzvah of sharing with the hungry and homeless has gone from the field to the market place to the supermarket.

One way our family could start a "tzedakah habit"

is _____ .

Sukkot In Jerusalem

Imagine that your family lived in the times when Solomon was king of Israel. One Sukkot you walk all the way to Jerusalem to be part of the celebrations. You stay in a sukkah. Draw a picture of your sukkah in Jerusalem. Draw all the celebrations.

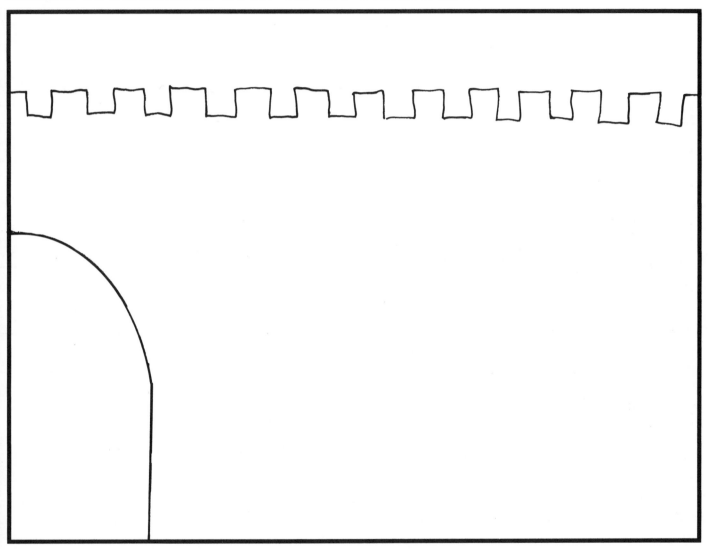

Complete these sentences:

1. After King Solomon built the Temple, all Jews used to come to_____ for Sukkot
2. They would bring gifts of thanksgiving to _____.
3. Jews came from all over.
4. Many of them camped out in _____.
5. Sukkot was a week-long party.

God

Jerusalem

sukkot

Ushpizin

Every night of Sukkot Jews invite famous Jews from history to join them in the Sukkah. Some Jews even bring an extra chair and pretend that their guest is at the table.

Spend some time talking about who to invite. Use the questions as guidelines. Parents should write down both their own answers and those of their children.

Children should ask their parents:

Who is one famous Jew you would like to invite to join us in the sukkah?_____

What would you want to ask this person?_____

Who is one person you read about in a book you would like to have join us in the sukkah?_____

What would you want to ask this person?_____

Who is one person from our family's past you would like to join us in the sukkah? _____

What would you want to ask this person?_____

Parents should ask their children:

Who is one famous Jew you would like to invite to join us in the sukkah?_____

What would you want to ask this person?_____

Who is one person you read about in a book you would like to have join us in the sukkah?_____

What would you want to ask this person?_____

Who is one person from our family's past you would like to join us in the sukkah? _____

What would you want to ask this person?_____

Our First Sukkah

My name is Ethan Kahn. This year was the first time that my family ever built a sukkah. They built it because I made them do it. It was my idea. I told my parents they had to do it. When I asked, I didn't really want a sukkah. It was just my way of getting even.

Last December, we went over to my friend Justin Wong's house. They are Chinese, not Jewish. We helped them decorate their Christmas tree. It was fun to hang all the colored lights. I dropped one of the silver balls and it got smashed, but they had extra. Justin and I got into a tinsel war. He had tinsel hanging from his glasses. I had tinsel down the back of my shirt. My big sister Rachel told our parents. We had to pick up all the tinsel and put it back on the tree. When we got home, I asked my parents, "Can we have a tree, too?" They said. "No." Then they said, "It is not a Jewish thing to do." I was a little mad.

This year in Hebrew School, we learned all about Sukkot. Our teacher said that Jewish families build their own sukkah. They eat in it, and even sleep in it. Our synagogue builds a sukkah in the court yard. The Jewish Center builds one too. Once we went and helped decorate it. I strung popcorn and helped to paint a big picture. But, I don't know anyone else who had a sukkah at home.

I thought it would be fun to ask for a sukkah. If my parents said no to a tree because it wasn't a thing which Jews do, they had to say yes to a sukkah because it is a Jewish thing. I asked, "Can we have a sukkah?" My father said, "No." I said, "Jews don't decorate trees but they do decorate a sukkah." My mother said, "It would be educational." Rachel said, "We live in an apartment; there is no place to put a sukkah." I said, "What about the roof?" To my surprise, my father said. "Good idea." Right away we all raced up to the roof. We found a perfect spot.

My mother called the rabbi and found out how to build a sukkah. My father and I went to the lumber yard. I asked Mrs. Wong if we could borrow their strings of colored lights. On Sunday, we carried everything up to the roof and started building. My mother cut all the wood. She wouldn't let me use the electric saw. My father stood on the ladder and nailed all the pieces together. My sister got to hold things for my father. I got to go up and down the stairs about fifty times. Whenever someone needed something, I had to go down and get it.

On Monday afternoon a truck from the park department dropped off some branches for the roof. I spent all afternoon carrying them upstairs. Monday night we decorated our sukkah. We had pumpkins and grapes and these things called gourds. We hung strings of popcorn and cranberries. Rachel brought the bird's nest she found at summer camp. She put it on the sukkah's roof. My mother hung packages of seeds. She said, "I always wanted to be a farmer." My father went down into the basement and took out his telescope. I didn't even know he had a telescope. He said, "The rabbi said you had to see stars through the roof." He also hung a star map on one of the sukkah walls. I took out the colored lights which I borrowed from the Wongs. Rachel said, "Our sukkah looks weird." I thought it was beautiful. We had the only sukkah in the world which was built around a television antenna. It stuck out of the sukkah's roof.

On the first night of Sukkot, we had a big dinner. Gramps and Nana came. I had to help Nana up the steps. We lit the candles but the wind blew them out. It was a little cold, but we put on blankets and hugged each other. I sat on Gramps' lap inside his big sweater. We played a game where we pretended that our sukkah was in the middle of the desert. We pretended that we were the Jews who escaped from Egypt. Nana told us all about the Promised Land.

On the second night of Sukkot the rabbi came over. He told us that our sukkah was real "kosher." He brought us a gift, our own etrog and lulav. He showed us how to shake them and say all the blessings.

On the third night of Sukkot it rained. The women didn't want to eat in the sukkah. Dad and I made these real big sandwiches. They were too big for me to bite all at once. We put on boots and raincoats and ate in the sukkah under Dad's golf umbrella.

On the fourth night of Sukkot we invited my whole Hebrew School class to come for dinner in a real sukkah. I was very proud. We played this game where we dressed up as famous Jews like Abraham and Esther and visited the people in the sukkah.

On Friday night we had Shabbat in our sukkah. After supper, Dad showed us how to use the telescope. We looked at the moon, Jupiter and the stars. I learned how to find the Big Dipper and the North Star. I asked Dad if there were any Jewish constellations. He didn't know of any. We made up our own. We found a menorah, Judah Maccabee and a bunch of stars we called the Matzah Ball.

On Saturday night, the Wongs came to dinner in our sukkah. Then Justin and I got to sleep out in the sukkah. We used the telescope and I showed him the Big Dipper and the Matzah Ball. We told some very funny jokes and stayed up real late. The sukkah was the best idea I ever had. Justin thought so, too. He asked his parents if they could have a sukkah. He said that they said, "No." I bet you they said, "A sukkah isn't a Chinese thing to do."

ANSWER THESE QUESTIONS

1. Did Ethan really want a Sukkah?   YES   NO
2. Did Mrs. Kahn know how to find out how to build a sukkah?   YES   NO
3. Did Ethan help his mother saw the wood?   YES   NO
4. Is there really a constellation called the Matzah Ball?   YES   NO
5. What was the best thing about the Kahn's first sukkah?_____

Use another piece of paper and make up your own Jewish Constellation.

The Lulav and Etrog

A Lulav is made up of 1 palm branch, 2 myrtle branches, and 3 willow branches. Which of these lulavim is correct?

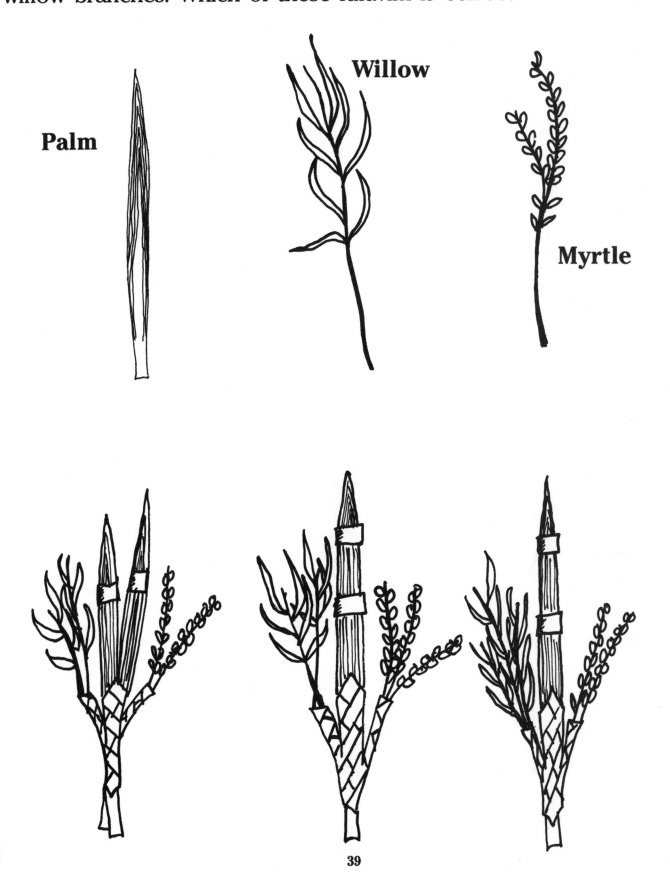

The Torah Service

Put these parts of the Torah service in the right order. Write in the correct number.

☐ Chanting the *brakhah* after the Torah reading.

☐ Taking the Torah out of the Ark

☐ *Hagbahah*: Lifting up the Torah so everyone can see.

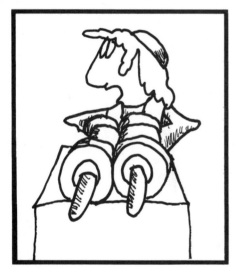  

☐ Chanting the *brakhah* before the Torah reading.

☐ The *Hakafah*: Walking around with the Torah.

☐ Reading the Torah.

When we do most Jewish things, we usually only say one blessing either before or after. Both reading the Torah and eating have two brakhot. One is said before and one is said afterwards.

How is reading the Torah like eating? _____

FOR THE PARENT
BUILDING JEWISH LIFE

A Partnership

This **Building Jewish Life** curriculum was designed in the belief that the best possible Jewish education happens only when the classroom and the home are linked. These pages are designed to cycle back and forth between those two realms, and to be used as a tool for learning in each. For this material to work most effectively, teacher and parent must assume interlocking roles and share in actualizing Jewish values and expressions. Each will do it in his/her own way. Each will do it with his/her own style. Together, they will reinforce each other, offering the child tangible experience and understanding of a visionary tradition.

Mitzvah Centered

Mitzvot is a word which means "commanded actions" and is used to describe a series of behaviors which Jewish tradition considers to be obligations. Classical Judaism teaches that the fabric of Jewish life is woven of 613 of these mandated actions. This series is built around the *mitzvot*, but it uses the term somewhat differently. In our day and age, the *authority* behind any "command" or obligation is a matter of personal faith and understanding. Each Jew makes his/her own peace or compromise with the tradition, affording it a place in his/her own life. In our age, the *mitzvot* have become rich opportunities. They are the things which Jews do, the activities by which we bring to life the ethics, insights, and wisdom of our Jewish heritage. Such acts as blessing holiday candles, visiting the sick, making a seder, comforting mourners, feeding the hungry, hearing the Purim *megillah*, studying Torah, educating our children, and fasting on Yom Kippur are all part of the *mitzvah*—Jewish-behavior— "opportunity" list. They are actions which, when they engage us, create moments of celebration, insight, and a sense of significance. It is through the *mitzvot* that the richness of the Jewish experience makes itself available. Without addressing the "authority" behind the *mitzvot*, and without assuming "obligation," this series will expose the power of many *mitzvah*-actions and advocate their performance based on the benefit they can bring to your family. It does so comfortably, because we know that you will explore this material and make decisions which are meaningful for you and your family.

The Classroom

In the classroom, this volume serves as a textbook. It helps the teacher introduce important objects, practices, personalities and places in Jewish life. It serves as a resource for exploring Jewish values and engages the students in "making meaning" from Jewish sources. The inclusion of both a parent's guide and a teacher's guide at the end of this volume was an intentional act. We felt it was important for parents to fully understand what was being taught in the classroom.

The Home

This material suggests three different levels of home involvement. On the simplest level, it contains a number of parent-child activities which demand your participation. They cannot be completed without your help. None of these are information-centered. The task of teaching names, pronunciations and facts has been left for the classroom. Rather, these are all moments of sharing values and insights or experimenting with the application of that which has been learned in class. They should be wonderful experiences and they call upon you to be a parent interested

in his/her child, not a skilled teacher or tutor.

On a second level, much of this material can also be used to provide "read-aloud" experiences at bedtime, or as the basis for family study and discussion at the dinner table. Do not be afraid to "pre-empt" that which will be taught in class, or to "review" that which your child has learned. The more reinforcement, the better.

Finally, and most dramatically, there is the experience of participating in the *mitzvot* described in this book. We strongly urge you to make this a year to "try out" as many of them as possible. Think of them as the field trips and home experiments which will enrich the classroom experience and make it comprehensible.

The Network

The prime focus of this text series is celebration. Celebrations are better when they are shared with friends. New activities and new challenges are easier when they are shared. Familiar activities are also enriched by the presence of others. Many of the congregations which adopt this series will already have a system of Havurot, Jewish Holiday Workshops, or family activities. Others will organize parallel parent education sessions and special events for the families of the students in this program. We also imagine that some families will network with their friends to "try out" some of these *mitzvah*-events. It is our *strong suggestion*, that at least on an event-to-event basis, you connect with other Jewish families to experience some of the celebrations about which your child will be learning.

Sukkot:

Origins

To understand Sukkot, we must speak of rain. For dwellers in city and suburb, rain often seems to be an interruption, something which keeps us inside—something which demands special protection. For residents of a temperate climate, rain also seems random; an occurrence which can as easily disrupt a summer's baseball game as melt the ice on the rink where hockey is played. To understand Sukkot, we must think of rain differently.

For farmers, rain means life. It nurtures and sustains the growth of food. The amount of rain is also critical. There can be too much of it as well as too little. If one lives in the land of Israel, rain is a somewhat predictable event. During the winter season it may rain; during the rest of the year it will not. Sukkot comes at the edge of winter, just before the rainy season begins. For that reason, it was once the most important single event in the Jewish year.

In its primal form, Sukkot was the holiday on which the Jewish people asked for rain. It was done with great joy and impressive pageantry. In Temple times, the week-long celebration of Sukkot was one of the year's two major pilgrimage events (the other being Passover). Jews came from all over the world to bring their tithes to the Temple, and to join in the celebrations. There were many special events. Every morning, after the burning of the regular sacrifices, there was a water-pouring ceremony. An imposing procession brought water carried in golden vessels up to the Temple mount where it was poured, along with wine, on the altar. These were major libations! Silver horns were blown, flutes were played, and a good time was had by all. The day was then filled with all kinds of special sacrifices—the impressive presentation of the gift-offerings brought by pilgrims from all over the known world. After dark came the fire ceremonies. Torches were juggled, giant *menorot* were set ablaze, and even the priests' old garments were burned in bonfires. Sukkot scored a ten in spectacle.

In one place in the Talmud, the rabbis make this central purpose of Sukkot clear:

> "Four times a year the world is judged. At **Passover** a decision is made about produce. At **Shavuot** a decision is made about fruit. At **Rosh Ha-Shanah** all creatures are judged. God, who fashioned them, considers all their actions. At **Sukkot**, a decision is made about rain."
>
> (Rosh Ha-Shanah 16a)

Agricultural connections pervaded the Judaism practiced in Temple times. Simple farm people wanted their religion to produce simple but effective results. Special gift-offerings, water-pouring rituals, and probably even the waving of the *etrog* and the *lulav* were originally cause-and-effect rituals to insure the coming of the winter rains. In our day and age,

the rain-making aspect of Sukkot rituals has been reduced. It consists only of the addition of one simple phrase to the regular daily service. Starting on *Shemini Atzeret*, the last day of this week-long celebration, the words "Who brings the wind and causes the rain to fall," are added to the second blessing of the *Amidah*, the long, standing, silent prayer. Subtly, by praising God for having previously given us rain, we hope to influence the continuation of that act.

For those of us who live in the wall-to-wall climate control of suburb and urburb, the Sukkot farming connection reawakens understandings which are too easily taken for granted. It forces us to reconnect with food hains and ecosystems, to reaffirm our awareness that despite our normal existence in carefully controlled environments, we are all passengers on "spaceship Earth." The rhythms and patterns of the natural order, and the quality of its equilibrium, will affect our lives. This is the first of Sukkot's important teachings.

The First Lesson: When we spend time in the Sukkah, we get a unique chance to experience the natural world. We are subject to wind and rain, hot and cold, sunlight and moonlight; birds and bugs directly interact with us—and that which we are trying to eat. We are reminded of our dependence on nature, and of our need to protect it.

Most full-fledged Jewish holidays are really two different celebrations which have been bonded into one event. Sukkot is no exception. As in most other cases, a historical commemoration is blended with an agricultural festival.

Sukkot is a two-fold celebration. In addition to anticipating the rainy season, Sukkot also serves as a reenactment of the exodus from Egypt. The Torah explains it this way:

> "You shall live in *sukkot* (booths) for seven days...so that future generations will know that I made the people of Israel live in sukkot when I brought them out of the land of Egypt." (Leviticus 23.42-43)

Like Passover, it is a holiday designed to give later generations a first-hand (through simulated) experience of what it was like when the Jewish people found their destiny. The outdoor living experience is a kind of Jewish "Outward Bound." It is a rite of initiation into the collective experience which shaped the Jewish people. This is the second insight taught by Sukkot.

The Second Lesson: When we spend time in the sukkah, we join in the experiences which turned a group of runaway slaves into a holy people. Being a Jew is owning Jewish history, and accepting a portion of the responsibility for our historic mission—the transformation of the world from a place of human slavery and suffering into a place of peace and prosperity. Sukkot creates a moment of living history.

The week-long celebration of Sukkot weaves together these two themes—the coming of the rainy season and the escape from Egypt. It is a merger of recognizing our dependence on God's involvement in the natural order with reliving the story of our national liberation. One series of celebratory acts has the potential to trigger a number of insights.

Three Opportunities

A classic story. After the second World War, a sociologist went to study local customs in Poland. She found one congregation where the unique practice was to walk on one's knees up to the *bima* when called for a Torah honor. Asking around the community for explanation, she was given a number of interpretations: It showed honor to the Torah. It acknowledged God's sovereignty. It gave deference to the community. Each of the practitioners had their own interpretation, their own "truth" about what the act had come to mean. Finally, the researcher interviewed the oldest member of the community, who revealed the "true" origins of this custom. Before electricity, a low chandelier had hung in the aisle. Kneeling was the only way to go under it.

The entire Jewish tradition, like the heritage of this single shul, includes a series of practices which have been preserved with layers of explanations and interpretations. Often, more than one understanding helps to make a practice meaningful.

Three biblical *mitzvot* define our practice of Sukkot. They are all found in one passage:

"(1) On the first day, you shall take the fruit of the *hadar* tree, branches of palm trees, boughs of leafy trees, and willows of the brook, and (2) you shall rejoice before the Lord seven days. You shall keep it as a feast to the Lord seven days in the year...(3) You shall dwell in *sukkot* seven days..."(Lev. 23.40-41)

You shall dwell in sukkot. A sukkah is a booth. Like most Jewish rituals, various rabbinic laws prescribe and circumscribe its practice. A sukkah must be a temporary structure. It must be built in the open, not in a room or under a tree. It must have at least two and one-half walls and a removable roof. The roof covering, called *skhakh*, must be made of things which grow in the ground. For the sukkah to be "kosher," the roof must be thick enough that more shadow than sunlight falls on the ground; and it must be thin enough that one can still see the stars through it. The sukkah's maximum height is limited to thirty feet. The sukkah's minimum height is set at three feet. Its minimum size is seven hand-widths by seven hand-widths. Simply, the sukkah is a temporary hut.

The implication of all these rules is that right after Yom Kippur, Jewish families should avail themselves of the opportunity to erect a foliage covered shanty in their back-yard, driveway, or other available open space. While the sukkah was mandated as a temporary shelter, the meaning of the word "dwell" was interpreted as really implying the obligation to live in it. The Talmud puts it this way:

"All seven days one should make the sukkah into one's permanent abode and one's house into a temporary shelter. How? If one has beautiful vessels, they should be used in the sukkah. If one has comfortable divans, they should be brought into the sukkah. One should eat and drink, and spend leisure time in the sukkah. One should also engage in profound study in the Sukkah." (Sukkah 28b)

Understanding the rules for building and dwelling in a sukkah is a relatively easy task. Explaining the custom is more difficult. Nowhere does the tradition offer a full or exact explanation. Instead we are left to discover our own insights. We have to follow the traditional migration from biblical text to rabbinic sources. The Torah explains the custom by stating, "so that future generations will know that I made the people of Israel live in sukkot when I brought them out of the land of Egypt." The Torah connects the sukkah and the exodus, but doesn't explain why it is important to know that they did so.

The Talmud struggles with that question. Its discussion (Sukkah 11b) ends in an argument between two of the rabbis.

Rabbi Eliezer suggests that the sukkah is a symbolic expression. When Israel went into the wilderness, they were led by a pillar of smoke by day and a pillar of fire at night. This was a sign that God was with them, to protect them. The sukkah was, for Rabbi Eliezer, a tangible reminder of God's presence and protection. It was a self-crafted religious experience.

Rabbi Akiva thought that the idea of building sukkot was to be a literal reenactment. When the Jews lived in the wilderness, they lived in temporary shelters. To relive that period of our development we should do the same.

And why relive that period? That, Rabbi Avika doesn't explain. He assumes it is obvious. Again, we are left to trace his reasoning.

The prophet Jeremiah offers this clue (2.2) when he voices God's thoughts: "I remember the devotion of your youth, your bride-like love, how you followed me in the wilderness.'' The desert period seems to be a kind of "honeymoon" period in the God-Israel relationship. The mini-exodus from home to sukkah seems to be a kind of spiritual second honeymoon, a return to the setting where the unique relationship was first consummated and bonded. One gets a better view of the importance of that time, when one looks at this midrash:

"The Holy-One-who-is-to-be-Praised led Israel for forty years in the wilderness, thinking: 'If I lead them directly into the Land of Israel, each family will become busy with its field and its vineyard; they will drift away from the Torah. Therefore, I am leading them through the wilderness. Here they eat a daily ration of manna, drink a measured amount of water, and the Torah becomes part of their bodies." (Tanhuma, Beshallah)

This rabbinic voice believed that the essence of the desert experience was the necessary common discipline which led to the evolution of a common value system. Sukkot, therefore, is a return to those basics. We recapture the past through the effort involved in erecting and decorating the sukkah; through eating, drinking, and studying in it.

The actual building of a sukkah is a relatively easy task. Simple and affordable plans can be found in *The First Jewish Catalog* (Siegel, Stassfeld and Strassfeld, eds., JPS, 1973, pp. 129-130). If there is a local Jewish bookstore or kosher butcher, you will also most probably be able to find one or more groups which sell pre-fabricated sukkot. A sukkah—self-designed or pre-fabricated—is something you will be able to use year after year.

All synagogues and many Jewish community centers build sukkot. If this is not the year to build your own, take advantage of the opportunity of joining in building and decorating a communal sukkah. Usually, the decorating is turned into a public event, a kind of modern Jewish barn-raising. It is a guaranteed good time to be had by all. Also, try to arrange time to eat as a family in a sukkah. This can also be arranged in most community sukkot. If not, the week of Sukkot would be a good time to camp out or have a picnic—anything to step out of the house as family. *This wouldn't fulfill the mitzvah, but it does touch nicely on the spirit of the law.*

We have learned from families who do build their own sukkot that the act comes with many suprising benefits. Family sukkot come to serve as science centers, collective projects, and personal holy places.

"What are you building Mr. Wizard?" "Why, it's just my sukkah!" Being in a sukkah means noticing clouds and stars, rain, bugs and lots of natural elements. It becomes the perfect place to do bird-watching or stargazing and to talk about how weather is made. Even decorating the sukkah has a scientific side. It has introduced many Jewish children to such strange growing things as gourds, squash, and cranberries. Hanging and decorating can also be exercises in practical physics.

"I'll go up the ladder and attach the walls with the electric screwdriver." "Thank you Ricky, but I'll do it. Next year you'll be big enough, but this year, just hold the bamboo in place." In the middle of winter, every Jew is envious of the fun other Americans have hanging and decorating. Sukkot is the Jewish opportunity to work together to create a thing of beauty. It is a family project which is much more fun than putting the storm windows up. A sukkah is one of the most fun things you can drag from the basement or the back of the garage.

"Don't be late for dinner, the Kaufmans and Uncle Dan's family are coming." "I thought they were coming on Thursday.""No, Jennifer's class is coming to use the sukkah on Thursday, then the Fogels are staying for dinner." Building a sukkah is just like building a private Jewish club-house. It creates an opportunity to invite lots of friends, Jewish and non-Jewish, participate in a number of events, and stage a week-long celebration which really lasts all week. A sukkah also creates wonderful quiet moments. It is a place where the whole family can have a meal, talk, and not rush for the TV. It is a wonderful place for quiet late night talks. It is a perfect place for afternoon reading. A sukkah can be a unique space.

On the first day, you shall take the fruit of the hadar tree, branches of palm trees, boughs of leafy trees, and willows of the brook. The *mitzvah* of using the *etrog* and the *lulav* is another carefully structured Jewish practice in need of intellectual explanations. The practice is simple enough. Three kinds of branches —palm, willow and myrtle—are bound into a *lulav*. A piece of palm is used for the binding. These are held together with an *etrog*, shaken and blessed. Jews shake and bless the four species daily (except for Shabbat) during Sukkot. In addition, during daily morning services there is a special choreographed version of Hallel, a collection of psalms of praise, which is accompanied by the synchronized shaking of the lulav and etrog. The ritual and blessing can be found (along with clear directions) in Michael Strassfeld's *The Jewish Holidays*, (Harper and Row, 1985, p.130), in the *First Jewish Catalog*, or in almost any prayer book.

An *etrog* and *lulav* are fun. You get to shake and play with them. They are one of Judaism's few prayer accessories. Even if you don't fully understand their function, you can still shake and bless with lots of enthusiasm. If you live in New York or Jerusalem, shopping for an *etrog* (the *lulav* comes with it) is lots of fun. There are big public *etrog* stands. All kinds of esoteric differences affect market value. You get to do a lot of testing and bargaining. Then you get to do a chorus of "my *etrog* is better than your *etrog*," because it has more bumps, a pointier shape, a longer stem, etc. In other locations, the shopping is done through a Jewish bookstore or synagogue. There is much less wheeling and dealing, but if you get there early (and get one of the first choices), you can still go for the gold.

The Torah doesn't explain this *mitzvah* at all. It just lists the four species and says, "do it." Anthropologists have suggested that the practice of shaking and waving the *lulav* has origins in an ancient rainmaking ceremony. In contrast, the rabbis evolved a series of allegorical interpretations. In most of them, the four different plants stand for different things: four seasons, four different kinds of Jews, different parts of the human body, the diversity of life forms created by God, etc. In others, the *lulav* is a symbolic scepter, a tool to aid the individual Jew when s/he appears before the Divine Monarch. Regardless of ultimate purpose, the *etrog* and *lulav* are fun. Go and find the best you can.

You shall rejoice before the Lord seven days. You shall keep it as a feast to the Lord seven days in the year. Sometimes the Jewish tradition is very considerate. Not only does it offer the opportunity for week-long celebrations, but it insists that they are fun. For urban or suburban Jews living in the modern era, the quick succession of fall holidays often seems like an imposition. However, like our perception of rain, what seems to be an interruption may well be that which nourishes and sustains life. Besides, who can complain about a *mitzvah* which asks you to have a good time?

Shemini Atzeret

If you turn in the Bible to Numbers 29 and begin reading at verse 12, you find a very strange set of directions. We are told that on the first day of Sukkot, the special gift-offerings in the Temple were to consist of 13 bulls, 2 rams, and 14 lambs. Following along in the passage, we learn that on the second day of Sukkot, the obligation was 12 bulls, 2 rams, and 14 lambs. The third day called for 11 bulls, 2 rams, and 14 lambs. And so it went, reducing the number of bulls daily throughout the holiday. The seventh day of this week-long celebration was to have 7 bulls, 2 rams, and 14 lambs. Then, the Torah describes (verse 35) the eighth day. We are first told, "On the eighth day you shall hold an *atzeret*, a solemn gathering, you shall not work at your occupations." This is a command which has not been repeated since the first day. Then we are told that the prescribed gift-offering is to be 1 bull, 1 ram and 7 lambs. The origin of *Shemini Atzeret*, the solemn gathering on the eighth day, is in this verse.

> Retelling the story of the human king and his banquet found in the Talmud, Rashi has the King turn to his children and say, "Children, I beg of you, stay with me one more day, it is so hard for me to part with you."

On Sukkot, only the first day is a public festival (calling for a day of no work). *Jews living in the Land of Israel and Reform Jews celebrate Jewish holidays for one day. It is traditional practice for Jews living outside of the land of Israel to celebrate "one-day" Jewish holidays for two days. Such is the custom with the first day of Sukkot and Shemini Atzeret.* The intermediate days, called hol ha-mo-ed, are days of celebration and sukkah dwelling, but work and everyday life go on. The eighth day of celebration is also to be a public—no work—festival. What the rabbis learn from this verse, is that "the eighth day is *not the last day of Sukkot, but is a separate festival.*" (Sukkot 47b ff) For this reason, the *etrog* and *lulav* are not used, there is no requirement to "dwell in the sukkah," and the small addi-

tions made in several of the daily prayers are shifted from the Sukkot insertion formula to new Shemini Atzeret inserts.

Now that we know that Shemini Atzeret is not Sukkot, we still need to understand its unique purpose. The Torah teaches us no *mitzvot* unique to Shemini Atzeret. It says nothing to overtly define the day's purpose. The only thing which gives the day unique character is its sacrifice of a single bull sacrifice in juxtaposition to the multiple bullock sacrifices prescribed for the seven days of Sukkot. When you count the number of bulls to be offered during Sukkot, the total is 70. The rabbis used this as a clue. 70 is Judaism's universal number. We are taught in a variety of midrashim that there are 70 nations in the world, 70 languages in the world, etc. In the Talmud, the juxtaposition is explained this way:

> "Rabbi Eliezer taught: To what do the 70 bulls correspond? To the 70 nations. To what does the single bull correspond? To the unique nation (Israel). This may be compared to a human King who orders his servants, 'Prepare for me a week-long banquet," then on the last day of that feast turns to his beloved friend and says, 'Tomorrow, prepare for me a simple meal that I may benefit from your company.'" (Sukkot 55b)

The word Hebrew word *atzeret* is difficult to understand. The 1962 JPS Translation, the New Jewish Version of the Torah, translates it as "solemn assembly." That makes the holiday's name "the eighth-day solemn assembly." Rashi, the famous medieval commentator, explains the word in terms of this Talmudic passage. He says, 'The word is derived from a root which means 'to hold back.' It is as if God is saying, 'I will keep you back with Me one more day.'" Retelling the story of the human king and his banquet found in the Talmud, Rashi has the King turn to his children and say, "Children, I beg of you, stay with me one more day, it is so hard for me to part with you." (Midrash is a flexible art form.) Rabbi Jacob Mecklenburg, a more modern scholar, uses Rashi's translation "the eighth day hold over" in a different way. He teaches, "During the holiday season, we have experienced a heightened religious fervor and a most devout spirit. This last day is devoted to a recapitulation of the message of all these days, with the hope that it will be retained the rest of the year." His insight is consistent with another midrashic tradition which teaches that the process of judgment begun with Rosh Ha-Shanah extends all the way to Shemini Atzeret. Thus, even though the verdict was reached on Yom Kippur, God "holds back" the verdict until the very end of this season, waiting and hoping for our repentance and growth.

The traditional opportunity to celebrate Shemini Atzeret involves setting a day aside and going to services. It involves the usual celebratory lighting of candles, kiddush and festive meals. Beyond these formalized observances, there is a secondary opportunity suggested by the midrash. If Rosh Ha-Shanah, Yom Kippur, and Sukkot have been significant events, then Shemini Atzeret is a chance to reexperience them for a last time. Think of it as the closing camp fire of a session at summer camp. It is a perfect time to sit as a family and remember what has happened during this holiday season. It might be a good time to "dedicate" the appropriate pages in the family album. Sometimes is fun to hold things over one extra day.

Simhat Torah

Jews read a piece of the Torah every week. It takes a year to read from every one of the 54 portions into which the Torah is divided. On *Simhat Torah* we read from the last portion and then the first portion in the Torah. It is a time of Mobius Torah, a practical exercise in showing that the cycle of Torah learning never stops. A simhah is a happy time, the time to give a party. Simhat Torah is the Jewish tradition's annual Torah party.

Simhat Torah is a Jewish holiday which experienced spontaneous generation sometime after the Talmud was complete and sometime before the major law codes were written in the 12th century. We know nothing about how it came to be. In this period, the rabbinic scholars of the Babylonian diaspora evolved the cycle of annual Torah readings. It was part of the process of making the synagogue the center of Jewish life. Simhat Torah was the crown of this system. With the Temple gone, with no more sacrifices taking place, Shemini Atzeret was the perfect place to graft a new practice.

Simhat Torah ranks with Purim as the time to come to services for fun. We sing and dance. There are parades (called *hakafot*). Flags are waved and having fun is encouraged. In *The Jewish Holidays*, (Harper & Row, 1985) Michael Strassfeld explains it this way, "The dancing calls upon us to throw ourselves completely into rejoicing with the Torah. It is a time of

dropping our defenses to express joy, when for most of us letting go takes place only at times of tragedy. To be able to express a fullness in relationship to Torah on this night will help us to express unmitigated love at other moments in other relationships. To dance like Zorba is a challenge to us all."

In our day and age, Simhat Torah has also taken on a new meaning. Simhat Torah is the one day each year when Soviet Jews gather in public. They have chosen this one day of pure celebration as the time to stand up to their oppressive society. Bill Aron tells this story of his visit to Archipova Street, the street outside the Moscow synagogue where Jewish Refuseniks gather and dance. "That night, a middle-aged man named Boris told us this story. 'I've been coming to Archipova Street on Simhat Torah for the last five years. It has been the one public way I have allowed myself to identify with the Jewish people. I never told the other members of my family where I was going or what I was doing. I wanted no harm to befall them. This evening, as I made my way through the crowd, I came face-to-face with my eighteen-year-old son. Our eyes met in recognition. He had been secretly coming to Archipova Street on Simhat Torah for the last three years.'"

To be able to express a fullness in relationship to Torah on this night will help us to express unmitigated love at other moments in other relationships. To dance like Zorba is a challenge to us all.

Footnotes:

1. *Sukkah* means a hut or a booth. The essence of the holiday of Sukkot, sometimes translated as "Tabernacles" is dwelling in booths. A detailed description of this *mitzvah* is found in the parent's material.

2. *Mitzvah*. As we mentioned earlier in the parents' introduction, *mitzvah* is a central word in this series. It is an ideological word whose explanation often defines the boundary between the various branches of Judaism. While folk-English reduces *mitzvah* to "good deed," and a direct translation presents us with the notion of "obligation" (coming from "command"), it is also possible to speak of *mitzvot as "Jewish things to do" or "Jewish opportunities." Regardless of your interpretation, this is an important word to make part of your child's Jewish vocabulary.*

3. *Pe'ah, She'khehah, Leket* are the technical names of three different kinds of tithes which Jewish farmers had to take from

their crops. (Don't worry, the middle name is indeed a tongue twister). The important lesson they teach is that with ownership comes obligation. In the Jewish tradition, part of the condition on which an individual was allowed to own a piece of the land of Israel was that s/he make a portion of the produce available to those in need. It was not an act of charity, it was a condition of ownership. Also, the food was left for those in need to harvest on their own. They got to work for their bread. Their dignity was to be preserved. These two lessons, modeled in these tithes, remain important.

4. *Ushpizin* is a folk custom evolved from the mystical tradition (Zohar 5.103b). It suggests that during each of the seven nights of Sukkot, a different "guest" from Jewish history would visit the sukkah. Special rituals were made up to welcome Abraham, Isaac, Jacob, Joseph and friends. These can be found in most traditional prayer books.

FOR THE TEACHER:

This volume of **Building Jewish Life** centers on these objectives:

Sukkot:

1. Students will be introduced to the *mitzvot* of (a) dwelling in the sukkah, and (b) using the *etrog* and *lulav*.
2. Students will explore how spending a week in the sukkah takes them back to when the Jewish people (a) spent 40 years in the wilderness, (b) were farmers who shared their crops with those in need, and (c) came up to Jerusalem to celebrate.

Simhat Torah

1. Students will prepare for the celebration of Simhat Torah by learning about and practicing its customs and by studying the first and last stories in the Torah.

Given the time available during the fall holiday season, we assume that in most cases no more than three sessions will be utilized to cover this material. Teachers should feel free to adapt and improvise according to (1) time available, (2) age and ability of students, (3) involvement of families, (4) previous background, and (5) moments of inspiration.

ESSENTIAL VOCABULARY

Sukkah	A booth or hut (plural: *Sukkot*, also the name of a week-long Jewish holiday)
Joshua	The Jewish leader who took over after Moses and brought the Jewish people into the Land of Israel
pilgrimage	a trip taken in order to perform a religious act.
Sukkot, Pessah, Shavuot	The three holidays when Jewish farmers made pilgrimages to Jerusalem
pilgrims	A person who is going on a religious journey. "The Pilgrims" came to America for religious freedom
Kohanim	Hebrew for priests," those who worked in the Temple in Jerusalem
Ushpizin	A custom of welcoming famous Jews from history into the Sukkah
Shemini Atzeret	"The Eighth Day Holiday," the celebration which follows Sukkot
Simhat Torah	The holiday on which we celebrate reading the end and then the beginning of the Torah
Simhah	A happy occassion
hakafah	Marching around with the Torah
aliyah	Literally, "A going up." Used to indicate moving to Israel and being called to the Torah
brakhot	Blessings
Hagbahah	The *aliyah* of lifting up the Torah

ADDITIONAL VOCABULARY

wilderness	Wild land where no one lives
orchard	A place where trees are grown to raise fruit
vineyard	A place where grapes are grown
bonfire	A huge camp fire

LESSON ONE: BASIC SUKKOT

1. **SET INDUCTION:** BEGIN with a guessing game. EXPLAIN that you are going introduce a Jewish thing and they are going to have to guess what it is. CLUE ONE: It can't be taller than 30 feet or shorter than 3 feet. CLUE TWO: It must have at least two and one-half walls. CLUE THREE: You can see the stars through its roof. CLUE FOUR: Its roof must be made of things which once grew in the ground. ESTABLISH that this is a sukkah. ASK students to SHARE everything they know or remember about the sukkah. INCLUDE that the sukkah is a temporary hut which Jews spend time in during the holiday of Sukkot, that the roof is made up of branches, that we decorate the sukkah with harvest things, that the Jews lived in sukkot while they were in the wilderness, etc.

2. **A PRETEND TIME MACHINE:** *This exercise would best be done in a real sukkah, otherwise you'll have to pretend that the sukkah is there, too.* MOVE the class close together. DESCRIBE the sukkah you are sitting in. POINT out the branches which make up the roof, the fruit which is hanging, the bird flying above the sukkah where you can see between the branches, etc. ALLOW students to play with the sukkah by HANGING pretend fruit and decorations. FEEL a pretend breeze blow. PLAY with the image.

REMIND students that Jews camped out in sukkot during the 40 years between the time they escaped from Egypt and the time they moved into the land of Israel. TELL students that we are going to MOVE the pretend sukkah to some place in the wilderness between Egypt and Israel. DIRECT students to look out of the sukkah. ASK them to DESCRIBE the Israelite camp. DISCUSS what the Jews ate during those 40 years. ESTABLISH that God had manna fall from the sky. EXPLAIN that manna tasted like anything you wanted it to. ASSIGN two students to go out collect the manna and pass it out to the whole class. HAVE everyone share what they are tasting in their manna.

REPEAT the process with a visit to a farm in ancient Israel. USE it as an opportunity to teach about the three tithes— *Pe'ah, She'khehah*, and *Leket*—found on page 8. SEND them out to harvest in pretend fields.

REPEAT the process with a visit to ancient Jerusalem during the Time of the Temple. You can find one description in the Parents'material. You can find a better description in *The Jewish Festivals* by Schauss (UAHC 1938). PRETEND to have a water-carrying ceremony.

RETURN the sukkah to where you began. REVIEW the three stops you made.

3. **READING ABOUT SUKKOT:** TOGETHER read from pages 3 through 12. STOP along the way to to CONNECT the things you read about with the things you pretended to do.

4. **THE HISTORY OF THE SUKKAH:** BREAK the class into three groups. ASSIGN each group to one of the three exercises found on page 30, 31 and 32.

This will be most successful if you ask a parent or teacher aide to work with each group. ALLOW students time to finish the work. ASK the groups to share both their answers and their pictures.

5. ARTS & CRAFTS: CHOOSE one of the following: (a) a minature sukkah made from a fruit basket or shoe box, (b) an ornament or decoration for the sukkah (home or congregation) made from the medium of your choice, (c) murals of the whole class and the the sukkah at the three places you visited.

6. CLOSURE: REVIEW everything you did during the day. RECONSTRUCT the three places you visited. ASSIGN students to complete page 32, A Home Harvest, with their parents.

LESSON TWO: ADVANCED SUKKOT

O. PROLOGUE: This lesson assumes two things: (a) that parents have been invited to join their children in this class session and (b) that at least some parents have been told in advance that they are going to play a character in a lesson (Abraham, Sarah, Isaac, Rebekkah, Jacob, Rachel, Leah, Joseph, Miriam, Moses, Aaron, Hannah, David or Esther). They should also be told to bring their costumes in a bag and come dressed in regular clothes. Depending on the community, you will have to weigh the comparative value of letters or phone calls explaining the roles. Also, each "character" should be given a one or two-page biography of him/herself. These can be drawn from an encyclopedia or from a children's book of Jewish heroes.

1. SET INDUCTION: WELCOME parents to the class. BREAK the class up into small clusters of parents and children. DIRECT them to read together the story on pages 35-37 and have them ANSWER the questions. PROVIDE each group with mural paper, pencils, aluminim foil and glue(sticks). Have them CREATE a star map with two or more Jewish constellations. BRING the group together. SHARE answers and results.

2. USHPIZIN: DIVIDE the group. SEND the parents (or just those who are going to play the "visitors") out of the room. MAKE SURE there is someone to work with them to EXPLAIN what they are to do. A Eabbi, extra teacher, well-trained aide or well-prepared parent can do the job. Each visitor should be ready to come into the room/sukkah when invited, introduce him/herself, tell a little bit of his/her life history, and answer no more than three questions.

Meanwhile, the rest of the class should be INTRODUCED to the custom of *Ushpizin*. READ and DISCUSS page 13 together. When you are ready to INVITE your guests, READ the following prayer. It comes from the traditional prayerbook.

> May it be Your will, LORD my God and God of my parents, to come close to us in this sukkah and to spread over us the sukkah of Your peace, to make a circle around us of your pure and holy spirit. Give enough bread and water to all who are hungry or thirsty. Give us many days to grow old upon the earth, the holy earth, that we may serve you and do your work. Blessed be the Lord forever and ever.

I invite to my meal the exalted guest _____.

REPEAT the whole prayer before each visitor. Have the class JOIN in saying "I invite to my meal the exalted guest." MAKE it into a kind of "Red Rover, Red Rover, send_____ over...."

3. PRACTICING WITH THE ETROG AND LULAV: INVITE to class someone who is good at the right procedure for shaking and blessing the *etrog* and *lulav* (or have one of these people train you). SHOW students the four different "kinds." Point out that this is the way we observe the *mitzvah* found in Leviticus 23.40ff (found on page 14). HAVE your guest expert show EVERYONE how to SHAKE the *lulav* and TEACH them the *brakhot*. LET each family practice this together.

4. EXPLAINING THE ETROG AND LULAV: EXPLAIN: "The Torah tells us that it is a *mitzvah* to shake and bless the *etrog* and *lulav*, but doesn't tell us why." ASK: "What lesson do you think the *etrog* and *lulav* teach us?" DIRECT small groups to figure out their own EXPLANATION of this *mitzvah*. Then, DIRECT them to read and discuss the explanations on page 14-15. ALLOW them working time. ASK the groups to SHARE their own interpretations.

5. CLOSURE: Depending on the timing of this lesson, GO OUT to the sukkah and either (a) decorate or (b) eat and drink. MAKE SURE a good time is had by all.

LESSON THREE: BASIC SIMHAT TORAH

1. SET INDUCTION: BRING a *Sefer Torah*, a Torah scroll, into class. Have STUDENTS rise when the Torah is brought into the room. UNDRESS the Torah and introduce the things which are used to dress it. LET students look at and touch everything (except for the calligraphy on the scroll). This can be reinforced with the Instant Lesson: *The Well Dressed Torah.*

2. READING ABOUT SIMHAT TORAH: READ together pages 17-22. GO OVER the words *Simhat Torah, aliyah,* and *hakafah.*

3. MAKING SIMHAT TORAH FLAGS: USE the art medium of your choice and be very careful about what you use as the stick part of the flag. Have every student MAKE his/her own flag.

4. LEARNING TORAH: REVIEW the fact that on Simhat Torah we read first the end and then the beginning of the Torah. TURN to page 23. READ together the last story in the Torah. You should READ most of the text. INSTRUCT students to READ the words in **bold** type. ASK students to retell what happens in this story. INSTRUCT them to COUNT how many times the word "land" appears in this story. *Move quickly through both of these stories.*

TURN to page 25. DO the same thing with the first story in the Torah. INSTRUCT them to COUNT how many times the word "good" appears in this story. Then TURN to page 29. QUICKLY WORK THROUGH this exercise as a whole class. ESTABLISH that these two words which are both repeated are the keys to parts C & D, the message of each story.

5. PRACTICING SIMHAT TORAH: WORK with the music teacher in your school. LEARN one or two songs for Simhat Torah. Then, take the flags and the Torah and have your own *hakafot.* Don't try to end this lesson, just let it dance away.

Anna Grossnickle Hines

WHAT
JOE
SAW

SCHOLASTIC INC.

New York Toronto London Auckland Sydney

Joe was the last one to line up
for the walk to the park.

So nobody saw what Joe saw.

4

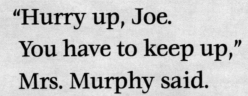

"Hurry up, Joe.
You have to keep up,"
Mrs. Murphy said.

6

But she didn't see what Joe saw.

10

"Come on, Pokey Joe,"
said Pete, who was first in line.
"You'll make us take all day."

But he didn't see what Joe saw.

"He's just a slowpoke," said Janet.
"Slowpoke, Pokey Joe," sang Dustin.
Janet, Pete, and Tisha joined in the chant.
"Slowpoke, Pokey Joe. Slowpoke, Pokey Joe."
"That's enough," said Mrs. Murphy. "Come on, Joe.
Hurry up now. We want to see the ducks, don't we?"

But none of them saw what Joe saw.

At the pond everyone crowded around
looking for the ducks.
"There they are!" screeched Pete.
"Where? Where?"
"Oh, there they are! There they are!"
everyone shouted.

Joe saw what everyone saw.

Mrs. Murphy got out the cracked corn,
and each child took a handful.
"Here, ducks. Here, ducks. Come and get it.
Come and get some corn," they called.

Soon Mrs. Murphy called, "Time to go."
The children scrambled to get in line.
Pete was first again, and Joe was last.

22

So nobody saw what Joe saw.

"Pete, you need to stop and tie your shoelace," said Mrs. Murphy.

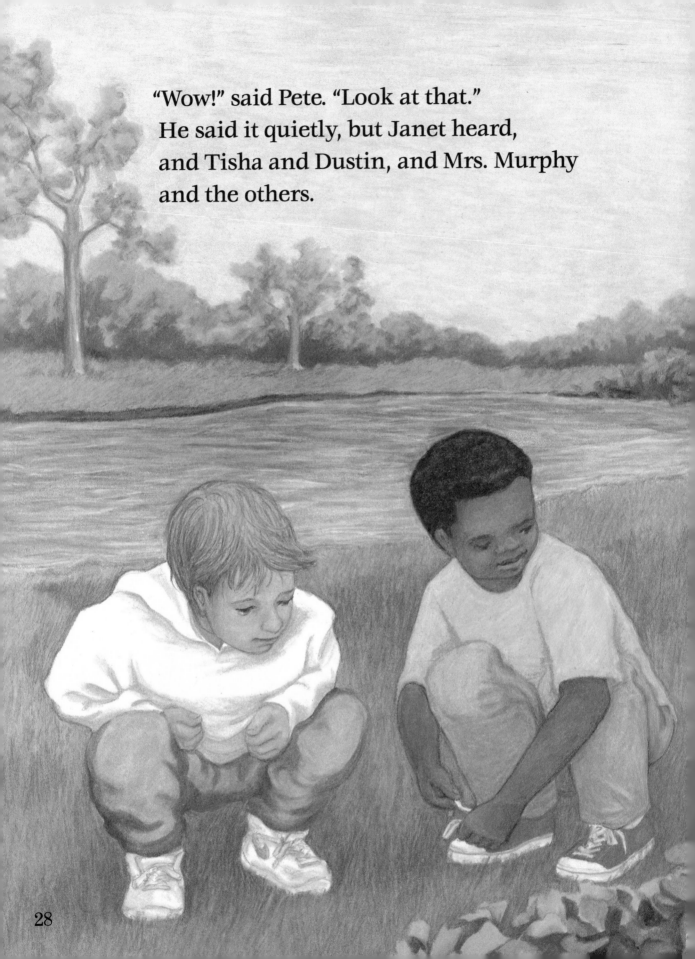

"Wow!" said Pete. "Look at that."
He said it quietly, but Janet heard,
and Tisha and Dustin, and Mrs. Murphy
and the others.

28

Then everyone saw what Joe saw.

TO SARAH AND NATHAN,
WHO TAKE TIME TO SEE

Copyright © 1994 by Anna Grossnickle Hines.
All rights reserved. Published by Scholastic Inc., 555 Broadway,
New York, NY 10012, by arrangement with Greenwillow Books,
a division of William Morrow & Company, Inc.

Printed in the U.S.A.
ISBN 0-590-63740-1

1 2 3 4 5 6 7 8 9 10   09   02 01 00 99 98 97 96 95

Watercolor paints and colored pencils were used for the full-color art.
The text type is Veljovic Book.